Fourth Edition

Test Manual for
APPLIED CALCULUS

S. T. TAN
Stonehill College

Prepared by

Robert J. Paul

Patrick Ward
Illinois Central College

Brooks/Cole Publishing Company

I(T)P® *An International Thomson Publishing Company*

Pacific Grove • Albany • Belmont • Bonn • Boston • Cincinnati • Detroit • Johannesburg • London
Madrid • Melbourne • Mexico City • New York • Paris • Singapore • Tokyo • Toronto • Washington

COPYRIGHT © 1999 by Brooks/Cole Publishing Company
A division of International Thomson Publishing Inc.
I⒯P   The ITP logo is a registered trademark used herein under license.

For more information, contact:

BROOKS/COLE PUBLISHING COMPANY
511 Forest Lodge Road
Pacific Grove, CA 93950
USA

International Thomson Publishing Europe
Berkshire House 168-173
High Holborn
London WC1V 7AA
England

Thomas Nelson Australia
102 Dodds Street
South Melbourne, 3205
Victoria, Australia

Nelson Canada
1120 Birchmount Road
Scarborough, Ontario
Canada M1K 5G4

International Thomson Editores
Seneca 53
Col. Polanco
11560 México, D. F., México

International Thomson Publishing GmbH
Königswinterer Strasse 418
53227 Bonn
Germany

International Thomson Publishing Asia
60 Albert Street
#15-01 Albert Complex
Singapore 189969

International Thomson Publishing Japan
Hirakawacho Kyowa Building, 3F
2-2-1 Hirakawacho
Chiyoda-ku, Tokyo 102
Japan

Printed in the United States of America

5   4   3   2   1

ISBN 0-534-35093-3

Table of Contents

APPLIED CALCULUS

CHAPTER 1
PRELIMINARIES

1. Find all values of x which satisfy the following: $|4 - 5x| \leq 7$.

   Answer: $\left[\frac{-3}{5}, \frac{11}{5}\right]$

2. Rationalize the denominator: $\frac{x}{2\sqrt{x}}$.

   a) $\frac{\sqrt{x}}{2}$ b) $\frac{\sqrt{x}}{4}$ c) $\frac{x\sqrt{x}}{2}$ d) $\frac{x}{4}$

   Answer: $\frac{\sqrt{x}}{2}$

3. Evaluate for $x = -8$: $x^{-\frac{2}{3}}$

   Answer: $\frac{1}{4}$

4. Evaluate for $x = -16$: $x^{-\frac{3}{4}}$

   Answer: $\frac{1}{8}$

5. Solve for x: $3 - 2x > 17$.

   Answer: $(-\infty, -7)$

6. Solve for x: $1 - 3x < -10$.

   Answer: $\left(\frac{11}{3}, \infty\right)$

7. Solve for x: $x \leq 4(2 - x)$.

   Answer: $\left(-\infty, \frac{8}{5}\right)$

8. Solve for x: $2(x+1)+5 \geq 3(1-x)$.

Answer: $\left[-\frac{4}{5}, \infty\right)$

9. Solve for x: $2x - \pi \geq 3x + \sqrt{7}$.

Answer: $(-\infty, -(\pi + \sqrt{7})]$

10. Solve for x: $6 < x + 4 < 10$.

Answer: $(2, 6)$

11. Solve for x: $-0.001 < x - 3 < 0.001$.

Answer: $(2.999, 3.001)$

12. Solve for x: $2 \leq -x \leq 16$.

Answer: $[-16, -2]$

13. Solve for x: $-1 \leq 1 - 2x \leq 1$.

Answer: $[0, 1]$

14. Solve for x: $-7 \leq 10 - 2x \leq -1$.

Answer: $\left[\frac{11}{2}, \frac{17}{2}\right]$

15. Solve for x: $15x^2 + x = 6$.

Answer: $-\frac{2}{3}, \frac{3}{5}$

16. Solve for x: $(2 - 3x)(x + 4) = 0$.

Answer: $-4, \frac{2}{3}$

17. Solve for x: $x^2 - 2x - 6 = 0$.

Answer: $1 \pm \sqrt{7}$

18. Solve for x: $(x - 5)(x + 2) = 8$.

Answer: $-3, 6$

19. Rationalize the numerator and simplify: $\dfrac{\sqrt{2} + \sqrt{5x}}{\sqrt{x}}$.

Answer: $\dfrac{2 - 5x}{\sqrt{2x} - x\sqrt{5}}$

20. Rationalize the numerator and simplify: $\dfrac{\sqrt{x}}{\sqrt{x} + 1}$.

a) $\dfrac{x - \sqrt{x}}{x - 1}$ b) $\dfrac{x}{x + \sqrt{x}}$ c) $\dfrac{1}{1 + \sqrt{x}}$ d) $\dfrac{x}{x + 1}$

Answer: $\dfrac{x}{x + \sqrt{x}}$

21. Multiply and simplify: $(x - 3)(x^2 - x - 2)$.

a) $x^3 - 4x^2 + x + 6$ b) $x^3 - 3x^2 + x - 6$
c) $x^3 - 4x^2 - 5x + 6$ d) $x^3 - 4x^2 + x - 6$

Answer: $x^3 - 4x^2 + x + 6$

22. Multiply and simplify: $(x - 2)(x^2 + 2x + 4)$.

a) $x^3 - 2x^2 - 4x - 8$ b) $x^3 - 2x^2 - 8$
c) $x^3 - 4x - 8$ d) $x^3 - 8$

Answer: $x^3 - 8$

23. Factor completely: $16 - x^4$.

    a) $(x^2 + 4)(x^2 - 4)$ b) $(x - 2)(x + 2)(x^2 + 4)$

    c) $(2 - x)(2 + x)(x^2 + 4)$ d) $(x^2 + 2x + 4)(x^2 - 2x + 4)$

    <u>Answer:</u> $(2 - x)(2 + x)(x^2 + 4)$

24. Factor completely: $x^4 + 2x^2 - 3$.

    a) $(x^2 + 1)(x^2 - 3)$ b) $(x - 1)(x + 1)(x^2 + 3)$

    c) $(x^2 - 1)(x^2 + 3)$ d) $(x - 1)(x + 1)(x^2 - 3)$

    <u>Answer:</u> $(x - 1)(x + 1)(x^2 + 3)$

25. Factor the following completely and leave all exponents positive in the answer.
$$x^2(x + 3)^{\frac{-1}{2}} + 4x(x + 3)^{\frac{1}{2}}$$

    <u>Answer:</u> $\dfrac{x(5x + 12)}{\sqrt{x + 3}}$

26. Factor the following completely and leave all exponents positive in the answer.
$$4x^2(x^2 + 1)^{\frac{-1}{2}} + 4(x^2 + 1)^{\frac{1}{2}}$$

    <u>Answer:</u> $\dfrac{4(2x^2 + 1)}{\sqrt{x^2 + 1}}$

27. Solve for x: $x - 2\sqrt{x} = 0$.

    a) $0, 4$ b) 0 c) $0, 2$ d) 4

    <u>Answer:</u> $0, 4$

28. Solve for x: $\dfrac{2}{\sqrt{x}} - 3 = 0$.

    a) $\dfrac{2}{3}$ b) $\dfrac{9}{4}$ c) $\dfrac{3}{2}$ d) $\dfrac{4}{9}$

    <u>Answer:</u> $\dfrac{4}{9}$

29. Solve for x: $2x^2 + 2x - 1 = 0$.

 a) $\dfrac{-1 \pm 2\sqrt{3}}{2}$ b) $-1 \pm \sqrt{3}$ c) $\dfrac{1 \pm \sqrt{3}}{2}$ d) $\dfrac{-1 \pm \sqrt{3}}{2}$

 Answer: $\dfrac{-1 \pm \sqrt{3}}{2}$

30. Solve for x: $3x^2 - 8 = 0$.

 a) $\dfrac{\pm\sqrt{8}}{3}$ b) $\dfrac{\pm 2\sqrt{3}}{3}$ c) $\dfrac{\pm 2\sqrt{6}}{3}$ d) $\dfrac{\pm 4\sqrt{2}}{3}$

 Answer: $\dfrac{\pm 2\sqrt{6}}{3}$

31. Solve for x: $\sqrt{2x-3} - \sqrt{x} = 0$.

 Answer: 3

32. Solve for x: $\sqrt{x^2 - 2} + \sqrt{x} = 0$.

 Answer: No solution

33. Multiply each pair of given expressions.

A. $(x-3)(x+5)$

 Answer: $x^2 + 2x - 15$

B. $(4-x)(5-2x)$

 Answer: $2x^2 - 13x + 20$

34. Multiply each pair of given expressions.

A. $(2x+5)(3x-2)$

 Answer: $6x^2 + 11x - 10$

B. $(1 - 3x)(2 - 5x)$

Answer: $15x^2 - 11x + 2$

35. Multiply each pair of given expressions.

A. $(2 + 3x)^2$

Answer: $9x^2 + 12x + 4$

B. $(1 + 3x)^2$

Answer: $9x^2 + 6x + 1$

36. Multiply each pair of given expressions.

A. $(x - 4y)(2x - y)$

Answer: $2x^2 - 9xy + 4y^2$

B. $(2x - 3y)(x + 4y)$

Answer: $2x^2 + 5xy - 12y^2$

37. Multiply each pair of given expressions.

A. $(3x + 5)(5x - 12)$

Answer: $15x^2 - 11x - 60$

B. $\left(3x^2 + 2y\right)\left(2x^2 - 5y\right)$

Answer: $6x^4 - 11x^2y - 10y^2$

38. Simplify: $(x + 3y) - 3(x - 4y)$

Answer: $15y - 2x$

6

39. Simplify: $\left(x^2 + 3x + 1\right) - \left(3 - 5x^2\right)$.

    Answer: $6x^2 + 3x - 2$

40. Simplify: $1 - (x+3)^2$.

    Answer: $-x^2 - 6x - 8$

41. Simplify: $(x-4)\left(x^2 - 3x + 2\right)$.

    Answer: $x^3 - 7x^2 + 14x - 8$

42. Simplify: $(x-5)(x+3)(x+1)^3$.

    Answer: $x^5 + x^4 - 18x^3 - 50x^2 - 47x - 15$

43. Factor: $10x^2 - 7x - 3$.

    Answer: $(10x + 3)(x - 1)$

44. Factor: $5x^2 + 6x - 8$.

    Answer: $(5x - 4)(x + 2)$

45. Factor: $6 - 7x - 3x^2$.

    Answer: $(3 + x)(2 - 3x)$

46. Factor: $6x^2 - 25x + 4$.

    Answer: $(6x - 1)(x - 4)$

47. Factor: $91x^2 - 246x + 143$.

    Answer: $(7x - 13)(13x - 11)$

48. Solve for x: $3(x-4)+7(2x+3)=5(x-2)-4(3x+5)$

Answer: $-\dfrac{39}{24}$

49. A salesperson for the Fintext Publishing Company earns a base salary of $125 per week plus a 7% commission on sales (S). The formula for computing a salesperson's gross pay (G) is given by: $G=125+0.078(S)$. Find the gross pay if the total sales for a week are $850.

Answer: $184.50

50. If the profit, P, from the sale of x hundred televisions is given by: $P=16x-15-x^2$, where P is measured in thousands of dollars, determine the profit from the sale of 800 televisions.

Answer: $49,000

51. Find the distance between the points $(1,-4)$ and $(-3,-8)$.

a) 8   b) $4\sqrt{2}$ c) $4\sqrt{10}$ d) $2\sqrt{5}$

Answer: $4\sqrt{2}$

52. Find the distance between the points $(4,\sqrt{3})$ and $(-1,0)$.

a) $2\sqrt{3}$ b) $\sqrt{34}$ c) $2\sqrt{7}$ d) $3\sqrt{2}$

Answer: $2\sqrt{7}$

53. Find an equation of the line through the points $(-1,0)$ and $(2,3)$.

a) $x+y-5=0$ b) $x+y-1=0$
c) $x-y+1=0$ d) $3x-y+3=0$

Answer: $x-y+1=0$

8

54. Find an equation of the line with slope -4 and passing through the point $(3,0)$.

a) $4x - y - 12 = 0$ b) $4x + y - 12 = 0$
c) $4x + y + 3 = 0$ d) $4x + y - 3 = 0$

Answer: $4x + y - 12 = 0$

55. Find the slope of the line $5x + 3y - 4 = 0$.

a) $-\frac{3}{5}$ b) $-\frac{5}{3}$ c) 5 d) $\frac{3}{5}$

Answer: $-\frac{5}{3}$

56. Find the point where the line $x - 3y + 4 = 0$ crosses the y axis.

a) $\left(0, -\frac{3}{4}\right)$ b) $\left(0, \frac{3}{4}\right)$ c) $\left(0, -\frac{4}{3}\right)$ d) $\left(0, \frac{4}{3}\right)$

Answer: $\left(0, \frac{4}{3}\right)$

57. Find an equation of the line through $(0,5)$ and parallel to the line $x + y + 3 = 0$.

a) $y = x + 5$ b) $y = x - 5$ c) $x + y + 5 = 0$ d) $x + y - 5 = 0$

Answer: $x + y - 5 = 0$

58. Find an equation of the line through $(-5, -3)$ and parallel to the y axis.

a) $x - 5 = 0$ b) $y - 3 = 0$ c) $x + 5 = 0$ d) $y + 3 = 0$

Answer: $x + 5 = 0$

59. Find the point of intersection of the two lines $y = 2x - 4$ and $y = x + 3$.

Answer: $(7, 10)$

60. Find the point of intersection of the two lines $y = 1 - 2x$ and $x - y - 5 = 0$.

Answer: $(2, -3)$

61.   What is the equation of the line in the graph below?

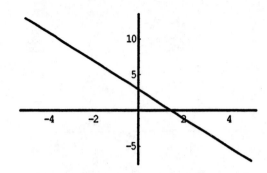

        Answer: $y = 3 - 2x$

62.   Find the x- and y-intercepts for $y = 6 - 4x$.

        Answer: $\frac{3}{2}, 6$

63.   Find the x- and y-intercepts for $2x + 5y - 10 = 0$.

        Answer: $5, 2$

64.   Find the x- and y-intercepts for $10 - x = 4y$.

        Answer: $10, \frac{5}{2}$

65.   Find the x- and y-intercepts for $75x + 250y = 10,000$.

        Answer: $\frac{400}{3}, 40$

66.   Find the x- and y-intercepts for $3x + 4y = 12$.

        Answer: $4, 3$

67. Find the slope of the line passing through $(-3, 2)$, $(5, 0)$.

Answer: $-\dfrac{1}{4}$

68. Find the slope of the line passing through $(6, -1)$, $(-4, 5)$.

Answer: $-\dfrac{3}{5}$

69. Find the slope of the line passing through $(-1, -4)$, $(-8, 3)$.

Answer: -1

70. Find the slope of the line passing through $\left(\dfrac{1}{2}, \dfrac{3}{2}\right)$, $\left(-\dfrac{2}{3}, \dfrac{1}{5}\right)$.

Answer: $\dfrac{39}{35}$

71. Find the slope of the line passing through $(0.4, -1.2)$, $(-0.5, 0.5)$.

Answer: $-\dfrac{17}{9}$

72. Find the general form of the equation of the line with y-intercept 5 and slope $-\dfrac{1}{2}$.

Answer: $x + 2y - 10 = 0$

73. Find the general form of the equation of the line passing through $(-2, -3)$ and slope $-\dfrac{1}{2}$.

Answer: $4x + y + 11 = 0$

74. Find the general form of the equation of the line passing through $(125, 400)$ and $(200, -50)$.

Answer: $6x + y - 1150 = 0$

75. Find the general form of the equation of the line passing through $\left(\frac{1}{2}, \frac{1}{3}\right)$ and $\left(\frac{1}{4}, \frac{3}{4}\right)$

Answer: $10x + 6y - 7 = 0$

76. Find the general form of the equation of the line with slope 0, passing through $(150, 60)$.

Answer: $y - 60 = 0$

77. If an independent truck driver's income was \$35,000 in 1989 and \$42,000 in 1992, and is a linear relationship, what should be her income in 1994?

Answer: \$46,667

78. If the profit is a linear relationship to the number of items sold, and a sale of 120 items gives a profit of \$466, and a sale of 200 items gives a profit of \$682, what should be the profit on a sale of 500 items?

Answer: \$1492

79. A rental car has a base cost plus a cost per mile. If it costs \$60 to drive it 100 miles, and \$104 to drive it 500 miles, what will be the cost for 420 miles?

Answer: \$95.20

80. Graph $y = \frac{2}{3}x$.

Answer:

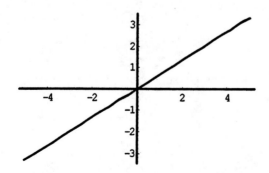

12

81. Graph $3y - 2x + 6 = 0$.

Answer:

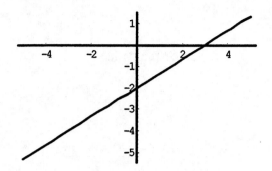

82. Graph $4x = 5 + 3y$.

Answer:

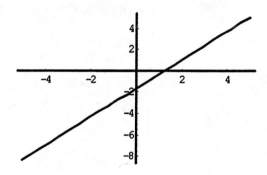

83. Graph $3x + 4y = 12$.

Answer:

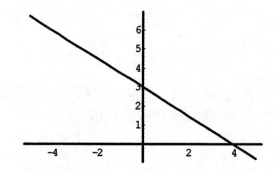

13

84. Find all values of x that satisfy $|3x+2| \le 8$.

Answer: $\left[-\frac{10}{3}, 2\right]$

85. Evaluate the following expression: $(-64)^{\frac{1}{3}}$

a) -8 b) 4 c) -4 d) Has no real value

Answer: -4

86. Simplify the expression: $\left(\sqrt[3]{\sqrt{p^6}}\right)^2$

Answer: p^2

87. Factor each expression completely.

A. $x^6 + 64$

Answer: $\left(x^2 + 4\right)\left(x^4 - 4x^2 + 16\right)$

B. $x^6 - 64$

Answer: $(x+2)(x-2)\left(x^4 + 4x^2 + 16\right)$

88. If $(3x+1)$ is a factor for all polynomials in both the numerator and denominator, factor the given expression completely and simplify.

$$\frac{(2+5x-3x^2)(3x^2+10x+3)}{(3x^2+7x+2)(9x^2+6x+1)}$$

Answer: $\dfrac{-(x-2)(x+3)}{(x+2)(3x+1)}$

89. Use the Quadratic Formula to find the roots of $6x^2 + 25x + 11 = 0$

Answer: $x = -\frac{1}{2}, -\frac{11}{3}$

14

90. Find the equation of the line that passes through the origin and is perpendicular to the line that passes through the points $(-1, 4)$ and $(5, 3)$.

Answer: $6x - y = 0$

91. Find an equation that satisfies the following:

A. The line passing through the point $(0, 0)$ with undefined slope.

Answer: $x = 0$

B. The line passing through the point $(0, 0)$ with slope equal to zero.

Answer: $y = 0$

92. For the line $2x + 2y + 1 = 0$, find the following:

A. The y-intercept.

Answer: $-\dfrac{1}{2}$

B. The x-intercept.

Answer: $-\dfrac{1}{2}$

C. The distance along the line from the x-intercept to the y-intercept using the distance formula. Rationalize any denominators.

Answer: $\dfrac{\sqrt{2}}{2}$

93. Find the minimum cost (in dollars) given that $3(2.5C + 4) \geq (5C + 22)$.

Answer: $C = \$4$

APPLIED CALCULUS

CHAPTER 2
FUNCTIONS, LIMITS, AND THE DERIVATIVE

1. Find the domain of the following: $f(x) = \frac{x-2}{2x^2+11x+14}$.

    <u>Answer:</u> $\left(-\infty, -\frac{7}{2}\right) \cup \left(-\frac{7}{2}, -2\right) \cup (-2, \infty)$

2. Given $f(x) = \frac{1}{6x+5}$, find and simplify: $\frac{f(a+h)-f(a)}{h}$.

    <u>Answer:</u> $\frac{-6}{(6a+5)[6(a+h)+5]}$

3. Find the domain for the function whose equation is $y = \sqrt{3x-1}$.

    a) $x < \frac{1}{3}$　　b) $x > 3$　　c) $x \geq 0$　　d) $x \geq \frac{1}{3}$　　e) None of the above

    <u>Answer:</u> $x \geq \frac{1}{3}$

4. Find the domain for the function whose equation is $y = \sqrt{4x+8}$.

    a) $x \geq 0$　　b) $x \geq -2$　　c) $x \geq 2$　　d) $x < \frac{1}{2}$　　e) None of the above

    <u>Answer:</u> $x \geq -2$

5. For $f(x) = -x^2 + 7x - 3$, find $f(-2)$.

    a) -13　　b) 7　　c) -21　　d) -12　　e) None of the above

    <u>Answer:</u> -21

6. For $f(x) = -x^2 - 4x + 8$, find $f(-2)$.

    a) 4　　b) 20　　c) -4　　d) 12　　e) None of the above

    <u>Answer:</u> 12

7. The total cost of producing x units of an item is given by the function $C(x) = 300 + 5x + 0.1x^2$, where $C(x)$ is measured in dollars. Determine the total cost of producing 100 items.

Answer: $1800

8. The total cost of producing x units of an item is given by the function $C(x) = 200 + 20x + 0.2x^2$, where $C(x)$ is measured in dollars. Determine the total cost of producing 100 items.

Answer: $4200

9. Graph $y = |2x - 1|$.

Answer:

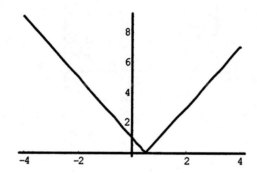

10. Graph $f(x) = x^2 - 3$.

Answer:

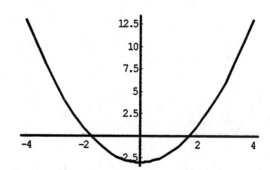

11.   Graph $g(x) = 25 - 3x$.

Answer:

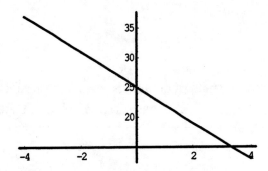

12.   Graph $F(x) = \dfrac{1}{x+4}$.

Answer:

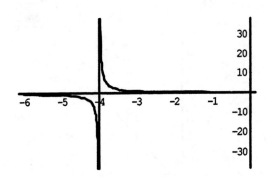

13.   Graph $y = (x-5)^2$.

Answer:

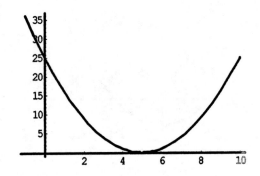

18

14. Graph $y - 3 = x^2$.

Answer:

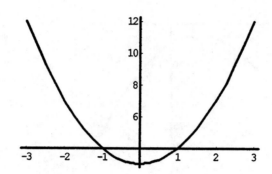

15. Graph $y + 1 = \frac{1}{2}x^2$.

Answer:

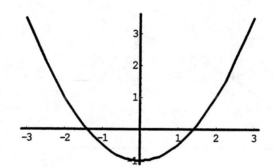

16. Graph $y = -2x^2 + 3$.

Answer:

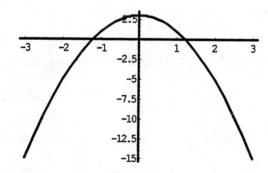

17.   Graph $2(x+1)^2 + y + 3 = 0$.

Answer:

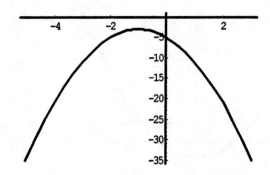

18.   Graph $G(x) = \sqrt{x+1}$.

Answer:

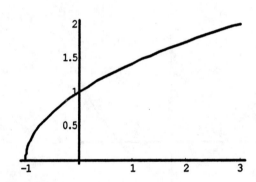

19.   Graph $f(x) = 2\sqrt{x} - 3$.

Answer:

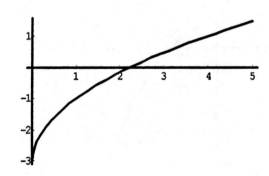

20. Graph $\begin{cases} x - y + 3 = 0 \text{ if } -3 \le x \le 0 \\ x + y - 3 = 0 \text{ if } 0 < x < 5 \end{cases}$

Answer:

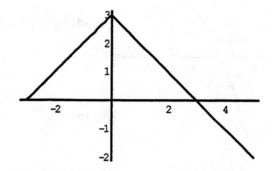

21. Graph $\begin{cases} y = 2x + 3 \text{ if } 0 \le x < 2 \\ x + y = 9 \text{ if } 2 < x \le 9 \end{cases}$

Answer:

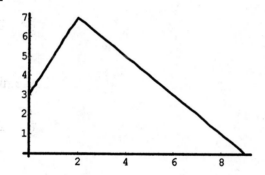

22. Graph $y = |x| - 3$.

Answer:

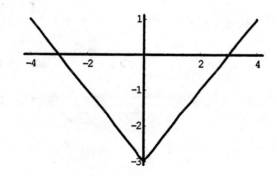

21

23. Sketch a graph of the following: $f(x) = \begin{cases} 16 - x^2 & \text{if } x < 4 \\ x - 4 & \text{if } 4 < x \le 9 \end{cases}$

Answer:

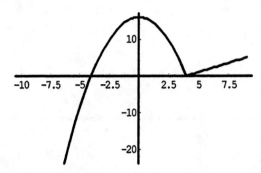

24. You are given $f(x) = \frac{1}{5}\sqrt{4-x}$ and $g(x) = \frac{1}{9x}$.

A. Find $g(f(x))$ and state the domain.

Answer: $\dfrac{5}{9\sqrt{4-x}}$; $(-\infty, 4)$

B. Find $f(x)g(x)$ and state the domain.

Answer: $\dfrac{\sqrt{4-x}}{45x}$; $(-\infty, 0) \cup (0, 4]$

Let $f(x) = 2 - 3x$ and $g(x) = 8 - 10x - 3x^2$. Evaluate each of the following values. Leave your answer in simplified form.

25. $g(a+b)$

Answer: $8 - 10a - 10b - 3a^2 - 6ab - 3b^2$

26. $f(t-h)$

Answer: $2 - 3t + 3h$

27. $g(x+2)$

Answer: $-3x^2 - 22x - 24$

22

28. $\dfrac{f(x+h)-f(x)}{h}$

Answer: -3

29. $\dfrac{g(x+h)-g(x)}{h}$

Answer: $-10-6x-3h$

30. A distributor can supply 6000 items when the cost is \$250 but cannot supply any at a cost of \$50 or less. Assume the relationship is linear and the domain is $[50,300]$.

A. What is the supply equation?

Answer: $p = \dfrac{1}{30}x + 50$

B. The demand is 5000 items when the price is \$50 and only 2000 items if the price is \$200. What is the equilibrium point for which the supply and demand are the same?

Answer: $(3000,150)$

31. After market research, it was found that the demand equation for a product is $200 - \dfrac{1}{20}x$ dollars, where x is the number of items produced. The cost function is $C(x) = 1000 + 0.5x$. Find the revenue function.

Answer: $R(x) = -\dfrac{1}{20}\left(x^2 - 3990x + 20,000\right)$

32. Find the following limit, if it exists: $\lim\limits_{x\to\infty} \dfrac{x^2+8}{6x^2-2x+1}$.

Answer: $\dfrac{1}{6}$

33. Evaluate: $\lim_{x \to 3} \left(3x^2 - 4\right)$.

a) 77   b) 5   c) 23

d) Does not exist   e) None of the above

Answer: 23

34. Evaluate: $\lim_{x \to 2} \left(4x^3 - 3\right)$.

a) 29   b) 5   c) 508

d) Does not exist   e) None of the above

Answer: 29

35. Evaluate: $\lim_{x \to 3} \frac{x^2 - 9}{2x - 6}$.

a) $\frac{9}{2}$ b) 0   c) 3

d) Does not exist   e) None of the above

Answer: 3

36. Evaluate: $\lim_{x \to -4} \frac{x^2 + 7x + 12}{3x + 12}$.

a) $-\frac{1}{3}$ b) -4 c) 0

d) Does not exist   e) None of the above

Answer: $-\frac{1}{3}$

37. Find $\lim_{x \to 5} \frac{x^2 - 2x - 15}{x - 5}$

Answer: 8

38. Find $\lim_{x \to 2} \frac{x^2 - x - 2}{x - 2}$

Answer: 3

24

39. Find $\lim_{x \to 1} \dfrac{x^2+3x+2}{x^2-1}$

Answer: Limit does not exist

40. Find $\lim_{x \to 3} \dfrac{x^2-5x+6}{x^2-x-6}$

Answer: $\dfrac{1}{5}$

41. Find $\lim_{x \to \infty} \dfrac{5x^3+2x^2-x+55}{2-3x^3}$

Answer: $-\dfrac{5}{3}$

42. Find $\lim_{x \to 3} \left(x^2-9\right)$

Answer: 0

43. Find $\lim_{x \to 0} \dfrac{x^2-5x+6}{x^2-x-6}$

Answer: -1

44. Find $\lim_{x \to 16} \dfrac{\sqrt{x}-4}{x-16}$

Answer: $\dfrac{1}{8}$

45. Find $\lim_{x \to \infty} \dfrac{x^2-5x+6}{x^2-x-6}$

Answer: 1

46. Complete the table below and use that answer to find: $\lim\limits_{x \to 2} \frac{x^2-4}{x-2}$

x	1.9	1.99	1.999	2.001	2.01	2.1
$\frac{x^2+4}{x-2}$						

Answer: 3.9, 3.99, 3.999, 4.001, 4.01, 4.1; $\lim\limits_{x \to 2} \frac{x^2-4}{x-2} = 4$

47. Complete the table below and use that answer to find: $\lim\limits_{x \to 2} \frac{x^2+4}{x-2}$

x	1.9	1.99	1.999	2.001	2.01	2.1
$\frac{x^2-4}{x-2}$						

Answer: $-76.1, -796.01, -7996.001, 8004.001, 804.01, 84.1$;
$\lim\limits_{x \to 2} \frac{x^2+4}{x-2}$ does not exist

48. The number of fish in a certain lake is given by the function $N(t) = \frac{2000t^2+100}{t^2+1}$, where t is measured in months. Determine the limit of this function as $t \to \infty$, which represents the upper limit of the fish population.

Answer: 2000

49. Sociologists have determined that the population of a town, $N(t)$, can be modeled By the formula: $N(t) = \frac{2000t^2+200}{2t^2+1}$, where t is measured in years. Determine the limit of this function as $t \to \infty$, which represents the upper limit of the town's population.

Answer: 1000

50. Graph the following function and determine the values of x for which the function is discontinuous:

$$f(x) = \begin{cases} \dfrac{2x+6}{x^2+7x+12} & \text{if } x \neq -3 \\ 2 & \text{if } x = -3 \end{cases}$$

Answer:

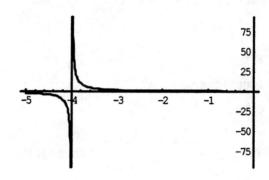

Discontinuous at $x = -4$

51. Suppose $f(x) = \begin{cases} 1-x^2 & \text{if } x < 3 \\ 1-3x & \text{if } x \geq 3 \end{cases}$. Find each of the following.

A. $\lim\limits_{x \to 3^-} f(x)$

Answer: -8

B. $\lim\limits_{x \to 3^+} f(x)$

Answer: -8

C. $\lim\limits_{x \to 3} f(x)$

Answer: -8

27

52. Consider the function $f(x) = \begin{cases} 2x+1 & \text{if } x < 3 \\ x^2 - 2 & \text{if } x \geq 3 \end{cases}$. Which of the following is true?

a) $\displaystyle \lim_{x \to 3^-} f(x) = -5$

b) The function is discontinuous at $x = 3$.

c) The function is continuous for all x.

d) $\displaystyle \lim_{x \to 3^+} f(x) = +\infty$

d) None of the above

<u>Answer:</u> The function is continuous for all x

53. Consider the function $f(x) = \begin{cases} 2x-4 & \text{if } x \leq -1 \\ x^2 - 5 & \text{if } x > -1 \end{cases}$. Which of the following is true?

a) $\displaystyle \lim_{x \to -1^-} f(x) = -4$

b) The function is discontinuous at $x = -1$.

c) The function is continuous for all x.

d) $\displaystyle \lim_{x \to -1^+} f(x) = -6$

d) None of the above

<u>Answer:</u> The function is discontinuous at $x = -1$.

54. Consider the function $g(x) = \begin{cases} x^2 + 2 & \text{if } x \leq 1 \\ 1 - 2x & \text{if } x > 1 \end{cases}$. Is g continuous at $x = 1$?

<u>Answer:</u> No

55. Exhibit an example of a function, f, that is continuous everywhere except at $x = 2$ but *is* defined at $x = 2$ and $f(2) = 7$. (The answer is not unique.)

<u>Answer:</u> $f(x) = \begin{cases} x+1 & \text{if } x < 2 \\ 7 & \text{if } x \geq 2 \end{cases}$

56. Find the value of b so that the function $h(x)$ is continuous at $x = 3$:

$$h(x) = \begin{cases} 2x - 1 & \text{if } x \le 3 \\ 4x + b & \text{if } x > 3 \end{cases}$$

Answer: -7

57. For what value(s) of x is the function below discontinuous?

$$f(x) = \begin{cases} \frac{x^2+1}{x^2-2} & \text{if } x < 1 \\ \frac{-12x}{x+5} & \text{if } x \ge 1 \end{cases}$$

Answer: $x = -\sqrt{2}$

58. Exhibit a function that is everywhere continuous but not differentiable at $x = 1$. (The answer is not unique.)

Answer: $g(x) = |x - 1|$

59. Does time, as given on a digital watch, describe a continuous or discontinuous function?

Answer: discontinuous

60. Does time, as given on a dial watch, describe a continuous or discontinuous function?

Answer: continuous

In the following problems determine whether the given function is continuous at all points in the given domain. Give any points of discontinuity.

61. $f(x) = \frac{x^2-3x+2}{x^2-8x+12}$, $-5 \le x \le 5$

Answer: Discontinuous at $x = 2$

62. $f(x) = \frac{x^2-3x+2}{x^2-8x+12}, \ -1 \le x \le 1$

Answer: Continuous

63. $f(x) = \frac{x^2-3x+2}{x^2-8x+12}, \ 0 \le x \le 5, \ x \ne 2$

Answer: Discontinuous at $x = 2$

64. $f(x) = \frac{x^2-5x+6}{x^2-x-6}, \ -2 \le x \le 5$

Answer: Discontinuous at $x = 3$

65. $f(x) = \begin{cases} \dfrac{x^2-3x+2}{x^2-8x+12} & \text{if } 0 \le x \le 5, \ x \ne 2 \\ -\dfrac{1}{4} & \text{if } x = 2 \end{cases}$

Answer: Continuous

66.   Let $y = f(x) = 3x^2 + 8.$

A.   Find the average rate of change of y with respect to x over the interval $[1, 1.6].$

Answer: 7.8

B.   Find the instantaneous rate of change of y at $x = 1.$

Answer: 6

67.   Find the average rate of change for $y = 2\sqrt{x}$ on the interval $x = 4$ to $x = 9.$

Answer: $\frac{2}{5}$

68.   Find the average rate of change for $y = 2x^2 - 3x$ on the interval $x = 1$ to $x = 4.$

Answer: 7

30

69. Find the average rate of change for $y = x^3 + 3x^2 + 9x + 27$ on the interval $x = -3$ to $x = 0$.

   Answer: 9

70. Find the average rate of change for $y = \frac{1}{x}$ on the interval $x = 1$ to $x = 3$.

   Answer: $-\frac{1}{3}$

71. Find the average rate of change for $y = \frac{5}{\sqrt{x}}$ on the interval $x = 1$ to $x = 4$.

   Answer: $-\frac{5}{6}$

72. Find the instantaneous rate of change for $y = 2\sqrt{x}$ when $x = 4$.

   Answer: $\frac{1}{2}$

73. Find the instantaneous rate of change for $y = 2x^2 - 3x$ when $x = 1$.

   Answer: 1

74. Find the instantaneous rate of change for $y = \frac{1}{x}$ when $x = 1$.

   Answer: -1

75. Find the instantaneous rate of change for $y = \frac{5}{\sqrt{x}}$ when $x = 1$.

   Answer: $-\frac{5}{2}$

76. Find the instantaneous rate of change for $y = 3x^2 + 9x + 27$ when $x = 0$.

   Answer: 9

77. In your own words, state the definition of derivative.

    Answer: Answers vary; the derivative of f at x is $\lim\limits_{h \to 0} \dfrac{f(x+h)-f(x)}{h}$, provided this limit exists.

78. Find the derivative of $y = 25 - 2x^2$ using the definition.

    Answer: $-4x$

79. Find the derivative of $y = x^3$ using the definition.

    Answer: $3x^2$

80. Find the derivative of $y = 5\sqrt{x}$ using the definition.

    Answer: $\frac{5}{2}x^{-\frac{1}{2}}$

81. Find the derivative of $f(x) = \dfrac{1}{2x-1}$.

    Answer: $-\dfrac{2}{(2x-1)^2}$

82. Use the definition of the derivative to determine an equation of the tangent line to the graph of $f(x) = \sqrt{3-x}$ at the point $(-22, 5)$.

    Answer: $y = -\dfrac{1}{10}x + \dfrac{14}{5}$

83. Find an equation of the tangent line to the graph of $f(x) = -x^2 - 9x + 5$ when the slope is -1.

    Answer: $y = -x + 21$

84. During the construction of a building, a brick is dropped from a height of 91 meters above street level. If its height (in meters) after t seconds is given by $s(t) = 91 - 4.9t^2$, find the brick's velocity at the instant it hits the pavement in front of the building site.

Answer: $-1.4\sqrt{910}$ m/sec

85. Find an equation of the tangent line drawn to the curve $y = \dfrac{4}{x+1}$ at $(1, 2)$.

a) $y = -1$
b) $y = -\dfrac{1}{2} + \dfrac{5}{2}$
c) $y = x + 1$
d) $y = -x + 3$
e) None of the above

Answer: $y = -x + 3$

86. Find an equation of the tangent line drawn to the curve $y = \dfrac{3}{x-2}$ at $(3, 1)$.

a) $y = -3x + 10$
b) $y = -3x + 6$
c) $y = 3x - 8$
d) $y = -3$
e) None of the above

Answer: $y = -3x + 10$

87. Find the instantaneous rate of change for $f(x) = -2x^3$ at $x = 2$.

a) -16
b) -6
c) -24
d) -22
e) None of the above

Answer: -24

88. Find the instantaneous rate of change for $f(x) = -2x^2$ at $x = 4$.

a) -10
b) -32
c) -64
d) -16
e) None of the above

Answer: -16

89. For $f(x) = 2x^2 + x - 6$, find the average rate of change of f from $x = 1$ to $x = 3$.

Answer: 9

90. For $f(x) = 3x^2 - x - 1$, find the average rate of change of f from $x = 1$ to $x = 4$.

Answer: 14

91. For $f(x) = 3x^2 - 2x$, find the instantaneous rate of change of f for $x = 2$.

Answer: 10

92. For $f(x) = x - 4x^2$, find the instantaneous rate of change of f for $x = -2$.

Answer: 17

93. Let $f(x) = x^3 - 2x$.

A. Find the average rate of change for f from $x = 1.9$ to $x = 2.1$.

Answer: 10.01

B. Find the instantaneous rate of change for f at $x = 2$.

Answer: 10

94. Let $f(x) = x^3 - 3x$.

A. Find the average rate of change for f from $x = 0.9$ to $x = 1.1$.

Answer: 0.01

B. Find the instantaneous rate of change for f at $x = 1$.

Answer: 0

95. Suppose the position of an object at any time t is given by $s(t) = -16t^2 + 32t + 640$, where t is measured in seconds and $s(t)$ is measured in feet.

A. Find the average rate of change of its position over the time interval from $t = 1$ second to $t = 7$ seconds.

   Answer: −96 feet per second

B. Find the instantaneous rate of change at $t = 4$ seconds.

   Answer: −96 feet per second

96. Suppose the position of an object at any time t is given by $s(t) = -16t^2 + 96t + 116$, where t is measured in seconds and $s(t)$ is measured in feet.

A. Find the average rate of change of its position over the time interval from $t = 1$ second to $t = 2$ seconds.

   Answer: 48 feet per second

B. Find the instantaneous rate of change at $t = 1.5$ seconds.

   Answer: 48 feet per second

97. Let $y = 4 - x^2$

A. Find an equation of the tangent line drawn to the curve y at the point $(-1, 3)$.

   Answer: $y = 2x + 5$

B.   Draw the function and the tangent line.

Answer:

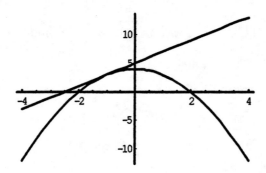

98.   Let $y = x - x^3$

A.   Find an equation of the tangent line drawn to the curve y at the point $(1, 0)$.

Answer: $y = -2x + 2$

B.   Draw the function and the tangent line.

Answer:

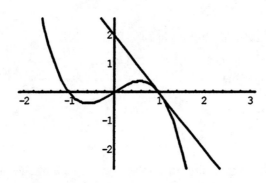

99.   Find the slope of the line tangent to the curve $y = x^2$ at $(1, 1)$.

Answer: 2

100.   For $f(x) = 3x - 2x^2$, find $f'(x)$.

a) $3 - 2x - h$ b) $3 - 4x$ c) $3 + 2x$ d) $2x - 3$ e) None of the above

Answer: $3 - 4x$

101. For $f(x) = x^2 - 8x$, find $f'(x)$.

a) $2x - 8 + h$ b) $2x + 8$ c) $2x - 8$ d) $8 - 2x$ e) None of the above

<u>Answer:</u> $2x - 8$

102. For $f(x) = x^2 - 2x$, find $\dfrac{f(x+h) - f(x)}{h}$.

<u>Answer:</u> $2x + h - 2$

103. For $f(x) = 3x - 2x^2$, find $\dfrac{f(x+h) - f(x)}{h}$.

<u>Answer:</u> $3 - 4x - 2h$

104. Let $f(x) = 3 - 2x^2$.

A. Find $\dfrac{f(x+h) - f(x)}{h}$.

<u>Answer:</u> $-4x - 2h$

B. Find $\lim\limits_{h \to 0} \dfrac{f(x+h) - f(x)}{h}$.

<u>Answer:</u> $-4x$

105. Let $f(x) = 4 - x^2$.

A. Find $\dfrac{f(x+h) - f(x)}{h}$.

<u>Answer:</u> $-2x - h$

B. Find $\lim\limits_{h \to 0} \dfrac{f(x+h) - f(x)}{h}$.

<u>Answer:</u> $-2x$

106. Find all points on the curve $y = x^2 - 6x$ where the tangent line is horizontal.

   Answer: $(3, -9)$

107. Find all points on the curve $y = 4x - 2x^2$ where the tangent line is horizontal.

   Answer: $(1, 2)$

108. The Puroform Company, which produces furniture, has determined that the cost of producing x chairs is given by the function $C(x) = 0.02x^2 + 40x + 400$, where $C(x)$ is measured in dollars.

   A. Find $C'(x)$.

   Answer: $0.04x + 40$

   B. Find $C'(20)$.

   Answer: $40.80 per chair

109. The Briteway Corporation, which produces lawn mowers, has determined that the cost of producing x lawn mowers is given by the function $C(x) = 0.01x^2 + 100x + 2000$, where $C(x)$ is measured in dollars.

   A. Find $C'(x)$.

   Answer: $0.02x + 100$

   B. Find $C'(10)$.

   Answer: $100.20 per lawn mower

110. Find $\frac{dy}{dx}$ if $y = x^2 + 2$

   Answer: $2x$

111. Find $\frac{dy}{dx}$ if $y = x^3 + 2x^2 + 10$

Answer: $3x^2 + 4x$

112. Consider the graph of the function $y = f(x)$ below.

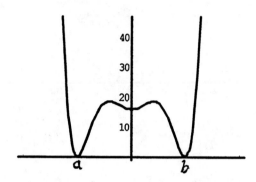

Which of the following statements are true?
    i) $f(a) = f(b) = 0$
    ii) $f'(a) = f'(b) = 0$
    iii) $f'(x) \leq 0$ if $a \leq x \leq c$

Answer: i) and ii)

113. Find the average rate of change for $y = 2\sqrt{x}$ on the interval $x = 4$ to $x = 9$.

Answer: $\frac{2}{5}$

114. Find the domain of the function $f(x) = \frac{x}{x^2 - 1}$.

Answer: $(-\infty, -1) \cup (-1, 1) \cup (1, \infty)$

39

115. Let the function h be defined as follows,

$$h = \begin{cases} x^2 - 2 & \text{if } x < 0 \\ 0 & \text{if } x = 0 \\ -x^2 - 2 & \text{if } x > 0 \end{cases}$$

Determine the following values.

A. $h(0)$

Answer: 0

B. $h(2)$

Answer: −6

C. $h(-2)$

Answer: 2

116. Given the following functions, find $f \circ (g \circ h)$ and $(f \circ g) \circ h$.
$f(x) = x;\ g(x) = x + 1;\ h(x) = \sqrt{x}$

Answer: Both are $\sqrt{x} + 1$

117. For $f(x)g(x) = x^2 + 2x + 1$ and $f(x) = x + 1$, find $g(x)$.

a) $x^2 + 2x + 1$ b) $x^2 + 2x$ c) $x + 1$
d) $x^2 + x$ e) None of the above

Answer: $x + 1$

118. For $f(x) + g(x) = x^2 + 2x + 1$ and $f(x) = x + 1$, find $g(x)$.

a) $x^2 + 2x + 1$ b) $x^2 + 2x$ c) $x + 1$
d) $x^2 + x$ e) None of the above

Answer: $x^2 + x$

119. Evaluate the limit, $\lim\limits_{x\to 3} \dfrac{(x-3)(x+3)}{x^2-9}$.

Answer: 1

120. Evaluate the limit, $\lim\limits_{x\to 1} g(x)$ where $g(x) = \begin{cases} \dfrac{1}{x^2-1} & \text{if } x \neq 1 \\ 0 & \text{if } x = 1 \end{cases}$.

Answer: Does not exist

121. If $\lim\limits_{x\to 2} f(x) = 6$ and $\lim\limits_{x\to 2} g(x) = -2$ evaluate $\lim\limits_{x\to 2}\left[f(x)g(x) - \dfrac{f(x)}{g(x)} \right]$.

Answer: -9

122. Evaluate $\lim\limits_{x\to 0} \dfrac{(x+1)^2-1}{x}$.

Answer: 2

123. Evaluate the limit: $\lim\limits_{x\to 2} \dfrac{3-\sqrt{x^2+5}}{x-2}$.

Answer: $-\dfrac{2}{3}$

124. For $f(x) = |x-1|$ evaluate the following limits.

A. $\lim\limits_{x\to 1^-} f(x)$

Answer: 0

B. $\lim\limits_{x\to 1^+} f(x)$

Answer: 0

C. $\lim\limits_{x\to1} f(x)$

Answer: 0

125. Determine all values of t for which the following functions are discontinuous.

A. $g(t) = \begin{cases} \dfrac{4}{t^2} & \text{if } t \neq 2 \\ 1 & \text{if } x = 2 \end{cases}$

Answer: $t = 0$

B. $h(t) = \begin{cases} \sqrt{-t} & \text{if } t < 0 \\ -\sqrt{t} & \text{if } t > 0 \end{cases}$

Answer: $t = 0$

126. Use the definition of continuity at a point to determine if the graph of $f(x)$ is continuous at $x = 2$.

$$g(t) = \begin{cases} \dfrac{x^2-4}{x-2} & \text{if } x \neq 2 \\ 4 & \text{if } x = 2 \end{cases}$$

Answer:
   a) $f(2)$ is defined
   b) $\lim\limits_{x\to2} f(x) = 4$ and therefore exists
   c) $\lim\limits_{x\to2} f(x) = f(2)$

127. Explain why the function $f(x) = \dfrac{x^2-4}{x-2}$ is continuous everywhere except $x = 2$.

Answer: $f(x)$ is a rational function. It is continuous at every point x, $(x-2) \neq 0$

128. Let $f(x) = \dfrac{x+1}{x-1}$ compute $f'(x)$ using the definition.

Answer: $\dfrac{-2}{(x-1)^2}$

42

129. Determine the equation of the line that is perpendicular to the tangent of $f(x) = x^2$ at the point $(1, 1)$.

Answer: $2y + x - 3 = 0$

APPLIED CALCULUS

CHAPTER 3
DIFFERENTIATION

1. The Department of Fish and Game has planted a species of sunfish in a new man-made lake. They estimate the population (in thousands) at the end of t years to be given by $P(t) = 2t^3 + 3t^2 - 2t + 2$ for $0 \le t \le 5$.

A. Find the growth rate at any time t.

    Answer: $P'(t) = 6t^2 + 6t - 2$

B. Find the growth rate at the end of 4 years.

    Answer: $118,000$ per year

2. Find the derivative of $f(x) = 2\sqrt{x}\left(3x^8 - 5x^6 + 9x - 8\right)$.

    Answer: $51x^{\frac{15}{2}} - 65x^{\frac{11}{2}} + 27x^{\frac{1}{2}} - 8x^{\frac{-1}{2}}$

3. Find $\frac{dy}{dx}$ if $y = 3x^4 - 8x^3 + 12x - 62$.

    Answer: $12x^3 - 24x^2 + 12$

4. Find the derivative of $f(x) = x^8$.

    Answer: $8x^7$

5. Find the derivative of $y = 5x^2 + 2x - 5$.

    Answer: $10x + 2$

6. Find the derivative of $y = -\frac{25}{x^2}$.

   Answer: $50x^{-3}$

7. Find the derivative of $y = 251,000$.

   Answer: 0

8. Find the derivative of $y = x^4 + 2 + \frac{1}{x^4}$.

   Answer: $4x^3 - \frac{4}{x^5}$

9. Find the derivative of $f(x) = -\frac{2}{3}x^4 + \sqrt{2}\,x^3 - 23x + 1005$.

   Answer: $-\frac{8}{3}x^3 + 3\sqrt{2}\,x^2 - 23$

10. Find the derivative of $f(x) = 5x^3 - 4x^2 + 5x^2 + 3x - 6$.

    Answer: $15x^2 - 8x + 10x + 3$

11. A tumor is in the shape of a sphere with radius of 5 cm. Find the approximate increase in the volume of the tumor if the radius increases from 5 cm to 5.1 cm.

    Answer: 31.4 cm^3

12. If a gas bubble is in the shape of a sphere with a radius of 10 millimeters and expands 0.2 millimeters, what will be the approximate increase in volume?

    Answer: 251 mm^3

13. Find the derivative of $f(x) = \frac{x^2 - 7}{x + 2}$.

    Answer: $f'(x) = \frac{x^2 + 4x + 7}{(x+2)^2}$.

14. Find the derivative of $f(x) = \frac{\sqrt{x}}{x^2+3}$.

Answer: $f'(x) = \frac{x^2-4x+3}{2\sqrt{x}\,(x+3)^2}$

15. If $y = 2x^3 - \frac{1}{2x^3}$, find $\frac{dy}{dx}$.

a) $6x^2 + \frac{6}{x^4}$ b) $6x^2 - \frac{6}{x^2}$ c) $6x^2 + \frac{3}{2x^2}$ d) $6x^2 + \frac{3}{2x^4}$ e) None of the above

Answer: $6x^2 + \frac{3}{2x^4}$

16. If $y = \frac{1}{2x^2} + \frac{2}{x^3}$, find $\frac{dy}{dx}$.

a) $-\frac{4}{x^3} - \frac{6}{x^4}$ b) $-\frac{1}{x^3} - \frac{6}{x^4}$ c) $-\frac{1}{x} - \frac{6}{x^2}$ d) $\frac{1}{4x} + \frac{2}{3x^2}$ e) None of the above

Answer: $-\frac{1}{x^3} - \frac{6}{x^4}$

17. For $f(x) = x^2 - \frac{1}{x}$, determine any value for x such that $f'(x) = 0$.

Answer: $x = -\frac{1}{\sqrt[3]{2}}$

18. For $f(x) = \sqrt{x} + \frac{2}{\sqrt{x}}$, determine any value for x such that $f'(x) = 0$.

Answer: $x = 2$

19. Find an equation of the line tangent to the curve $y = \frac{x}{x+1}$ at the origin.

a) $x + y = 0$ b) $x - y = 0$ c) $x - y + 1 = 0$ d) $x - y - 1 = 0$ e) None of the above

Answer: $x - y = 0$

20. Find an equation of the line tangent to the curve $y = \frac{x+1}{x^2}$ at the point (1,2).

 a) $3x + y - 5 = 0$ b) $x + y - 3 = 0$ c) $5x + y - 3 = 0$
 d) $x + y + 3 = 0$ e) None of the above

Answer: $3x + y - 5 = 0$

21. Given $f(x) = \frac{x^2}{3-x}$, for what value(s) of x does $f'(x) = 0$?

 a) 0, 3 b) 0, 6 c) $\pm\sqrt{6}$ d) 0, 2 e) None of the above

Answer: 0, 6

22. Given $f(x) = \frac{x+1}{x^2}$, for what value(s) of x does $f'(x) = 0$?

 a) –2 b) 2 c) 0 d) –1 e) None of the above

Answer: –2

23. Find $f'(x)$ if $f(x) = \frac{1}{4x}\left(x^2 + x^{-2}\right)$.

Answer: $\frac{x^4 - 3}{4x^4}$

24. Find $g'(t)$ if $g(t) = \frac{2t+3}{t^2+1}$.

Answer: $\frac{2 - 6t - 2t^2}{(t+1)^2}$

25. If $f(x) = \frac{1}{x^2+1}$, find $f'(2)$.

 a) $\frac{1}{4}$ b) $-\frac{1}{25}$ c) $-\frac{4}{25}$ d) $\frac{1}{25}$ e) None of the above

Answer: $-\frac{4}{25}$

26. If $f(x) = \frac{2}{1-x^3}$, find $f'(-1)$.

a) $-\frac{1}{2}$ b) $\frac{3}{2}$ c) $-\frac{3}{2}$ d) $\frac{5}{4}$ e) None of the above

Answer: $\frac{3}{2}$

27. For $f(x) = \frac{x^3}{4-x}$, find $f'(2)$.

Answer: 8

28. For $f(x) = \frac{x}{1-x^3}$, find $f'(2)$.

Answer: $\frac{17}{49}$

29. In an experiment involving an unidentified virus, researchers have determined that the body temperature (B) of a victim varies with respect to time (t) and is approximated by $B = \frac{10t}{t^2+1} + 98.6$, where B is measured in degrees Fahrenheit and t is measured in hours. Determine the rate of change of body temperature with respect to time.

Answer: $\frac{dB}{dt} = \frac{10-10t^2}{(t^2+1)^2}$

30. A marine biologist is running experiments involving the environmental temperature for a particular species of fish. The appetite (A) of the fish seems to be affected by the temperature (T) of water and can be approximated by $A = \frac{5000}{T^2+1}$, $50^\circ \le T \le 80^\circ$, where $A = 1$ is considered normal appetite. Find the rate of change in appetite with respect to the temperature when the temperature is 60°.

Answer: -0.0463

31. Find the derivative of $y = 6x^4(x^2 - 3x + 5)$.

Answer: $6x^3(6x^2 - 15x + 20)$

32. Find the derivative of $y = (3 - 5x)(x - 5)$.

Answer: $-10x + 28$

33. Find the derivative of $y = \frac{x+3}{x-4}$.

Answer: $-\dfrac{7}{(x-4)^2}$

34. Find the derivative of $y = \frac{x^2-5x+6}{x^2-x-6}$.

Answer: $\dfrac{4}{(x+2)^2}$

35. Find the derivative of $y = \frac{x^2-5}{2x^2+3}$.

Answer: $\dfrac{26x}{(2x^2+3)^2}$

36. Find the slope of the line tangent to the curve $f(x) = \frac{x-5}{x^2+1}$ at $x = 1$.

Answer: $\dfrac{5}{2}$

37. Find the derivative of $f(x) = 4x^4(4x^3 + 1)^7$.

Answer: $16x^3(4x^3 + 1)^6(25x^3 + 1)$

38. If $f(x) = 2x\sqrt{x+4}$, find $f'(0)$.

a) 0   b) 4   c) 2   d) $\frac{1}{2}$ e) None of the above

Answer: 4

49

39. If $f(x) = \sqrt[3]{1 - 2x}$, find $f'(0)$.

a) $\frac{1}{3}$ b) $\frac{2}{3}$ c) $-\frac{1}{3}$ d) $-\frac{2}{3}$ e) None of the above

Answer: $-\frac{2}{3}$

40. If $f(x) = -2[g(x)]^4$, then which expression represents $f'(x)$?

a) $-8[g(x)]^3 \cdot g'(x)$ b) $-8[g(x)]^3$ c) $4[-2g(x)]^3 \cdot g'(x)$

d) $-8[g'(x)]^3 \cdot g'(x)$ e) None of the above

Answer: $-8[g(x)]^3 \cdot g'(x)$

41. If $f(x) = 3\sqrt{g(x)}$, then which expression represents $f'(x)$?

a) $\dfrac{3}{2\sqrt{g(x)}}$ b) $\dfrac{3g'(x)}{2\sqrt{g(x)}}$ c) $\dfrac{3}{2g'(x)\sqrt{g(x)}}$

d) $\dfrac{3}{2\sqrt{g'(x)}}$ e) None of the above

Answer: $\dfrac{3g'(x)}{2\sqrt{g(x)}}$

42. If $y = x^2(x+1)^4$, find $\dfrac{dy}{dx}$.

a) $8x(x+1)^3$ b) $4x^2(x+1)^3$ c) $2x(x+1)^3(3x+1)$

d) $4x(x+1)^3(2x+1)$ e) None of the above

Answer: $2x(x+1)^3(3x+1)$

43. If $y = \sqrt{x}\,(x+1)^3$, find $\dfrac{dy}{dx}$.

a) $\dfrac{(x+1)^2(7x+1)}{2\sqrt{x}}$

b) $\dfrac{(x+1)^2(5x+2)}{2\sqrt{x}}$

c) $\dfrac{3x(x+1)^3}{2\sqrt{x}}$

d) $\dfrac{3(x+1)^2}{2\sqrt{x}}$

e) None of the above

Answer: $\dfrac{(x+1)^2(7x+1)}{2\sqrt{x}}$

44. If $y = 1 - u^2$ and $u = \dfrac{1}{x}$, find $\dfrac{dy}{dx}$

a) $\dfrac{2}{x^3}$

b) $\dfrac{2}{x}$

c) $-\dfrac{2}{x^3}$

d) $2x$

e) None of the above

Answer: $\dfrac{2}{x^3}$

45. If $y = \dfrac{1}{u+1}$ and $u = \sqrt{x}$, find $\dfrac{dy}{dx}$

a) $\dfrac{-1}{2x\sqrt{x}}$

b) $\dfrac{-1}{2\sqrt{x}\,(\sqrt{x}+1)^2}$

c) $-\dfrac{1}{(\sqrt{x}+1)^2}$

d) $\dfrac{-2\sqrt{x}}{(\sqrt{x}+1)^2}$

e) None of the above

Answer: $\dfrac{-1}{2\sqrt{x}\,(\sqrt{x}+1)^2}$

46. For $f(x) = x\sqrt{x^2-1}$, find $f'(x)$.

Answer: $\left(x^2-1\right)^{\frac{-1}{2}}\left(2x^2-1\right)$

47. For $f(x) = 3x\sqrt[3]{x+1}$, find $f'(x)$.

Answer: $(x+1)^{\frac{-2}{3}}(4x+3)$

48. Find the derivative of $y = \sqrt{x}\,(x-4)^{-2}$.

Answer: $-\frac{1}{2}x^{-\frac{1}{2}}(x-4)^{-3}(3x+4)$

49. Find the derivative of $f(x) = \dfrac{4x+1}{\sqrt{x+2}}$.

Answer: $\dfrac{4x+15}{2(x+2)^{\frac{3}{2}}}$

50. Find the derivative of $f(x) = \left(3x^2 + 4x - 1\right)^3$.

Answer: $6(3x+2)\left(3x^2 + 4x - 1\right)^2$

51. Find the derivative of $y = \left(3x^3 + 4\right)^{\frac{1}{9}}$.

Answer: $3x^2\left(3x^3 + 4\right)^{-\frac{8}{9}}$

52. Find the derivative of $y = \dfrac{(3x^2-5)^3}{(x^2+2)^2}$.

Answer: $\dfrac{2x(3x^2-5)^2(6x^2+23)}{(x^2+2)^2}$

53. Find the derivative of $f(x) = \left(3x^2 + 1\right)^4(2-5x)^2$.

Answer: $-2(2-5x)\left(3x^2+1\right)^3\left(75x^2 - 24x + 5\right)$

54. Find the derivative of $y = \dfrac{1}{(x+3)^3}$.

Answer: $-\dfrac{3}{(x+3)^4}$

55. Find the derivative of $y = 3\sqrt[3]{x}\left(4x^{-2} + x^{-1} + 3\right)$

Answer: $-20x^{-\frac{5}{3}} - 2x^{-\frac{5}{3}} + 3x^{-\frac{2}{3}}$

56. Find the slope of the line tangent to the curve $y = 3x^2(3 - 2x)^4$ at $x = 0$.

Answer: 0

57. The manufacturers of a certain product have found the weekly demand for their product is $p = -0.07x + 100$ and their weekly profit can be determined by $P(x) = x^3 - x^2 + 9x - 900$.

A. Find the company's average weekly cost function $A(x)$.

Answer: $A(x) = -x^2 + 0.93x + 91 + \dfrac{900}{x}$

B. Find the company's weekly marginal average cost function $A'(x)$.

Answer: $A'(x) = -2x + 0.93 - \dfrac{900}{x^2}$

58. The revenue from production and selling x hundred units of a product is $R(x) = 10\sqrt{3x + 1}$, where $R(x)$ is measured in hundreds of dollars. Find the marginal revenue for 500 units of the product being produced and sold.

Answer: $375

59. The Permalite Flashlight Company has determined that the daily profit from production and selling x hundred flashlights is given by $P(x) = 10(x - 5)^3 - 100x + 800$, where $P(x)$ is measured in dollars. Determine the marginal profit for 300 flashlights.

Answer: $20 per flashlight

60.   The Ivonic Heater Company has determined that the cost of producing x space heaters per day is given by $C(x) = 0.01x^2 - 0.8x + 16.5$, where $C(x)$ is measured in thousands of dollars.

A.   Find the marginal cost.

       Answer: $C'(x) = 0.02x - 0.8$

B.   Find $C'(40)$.

       Answer: 0

C. Find $C'(41)$.

       Answer: $20 per heater

61.   Suppose that the demand equation for a certain product is given by $p = 115 - 0.2x$ and the cost is given by $C(x) = 1200 + 5x$.

A.   Find $R(x)$.

       Answer: $110x - 0.2x^2$

B.   Find $P(x)$.

       Answer: $100x - 0.2x^2 - 1200$

C.   Find $P'(x)$.

       Answer: $110 - 0.4x$

62.   If the demand equation for a particular product is $f(p) = 1200 - 4p$, find the elasticity of demand.

       a) –4   b) $\dfrac{1}{p-300}$ c) $-\dfrac{1}{300}$ d) $\dfrac{p}{p-300}$ e) None of the above

       Answer: $\dfrac{p}{p-300}$

63. If the demand equation for a particular product is $f(p) = 4800 - 8p$, find the elasticity of demand.

a) -8 b) $\dfrac{1}{p-600}$ c) $-\dfrac{1}{600}$ d) $\dfrac{p}{p-600}$ e) None of the above

Answer: $\dfrac{p}{p-600}$

64. If the demand equation is given by $f(p) = 3600 - 4p^2$, then at $p = \$20$, demand is elastic.

a) True   b) False

Answer: True

65. If the demand equation is given by $f(p) = 5000 - 2p^2$, then at $p = \$20$, demand is inelastic.

a) True   b) False

Answer: True

66. If the profit, P in dollars, for a company is a function of the number of units produced, x, it can be determined that it approximates the function $P(x) = \dfrac{1000 - x^2}{5 - x^2}$. If the current level of production is 100 units, what is the per unit increase in profit if production is increased from 100 to 110 units?

Answer: about $\$0.02$

67. If the profit, P in dollars, for a company is a function of the number of units produced, x, it can be determined that it approximates the function $P(x) = \dfrac{1000 - x^2}{5 - x^2}$. Find the marginal profit.

Answer: $1990x\left(5 - x^2\right)^{-2}$

68. Find all derivatives of $y = 1 - 3x^4$.

Answer: $y' = -12x^3$; $y'' = -36x^2$; $y''' = -72x$; $y^{(iv)} = -72$; all the rest are zero

55

69. Find the first four derivatives of $y = \frac{x-1}{2x^2}$.

Answer:
$$y' = -\frac{1}{2}x^{-2} + x^{-3}; \; y'' = x^{-3} - 3x^{-4}; \; y''' = -3x^{-4} + 12x^{-5}; \; y^{(iv)} = 12x^{-5} - 60x^{-6}$$

70. Find the first four derivatives of $y = 3x^{\frac{1}{3}}$.

Answer:
$$y' = x^{-\frac{2}{3}}; \; y'' = -\frac{2}{3}x^{-\frac{5}{3}}; \; y''' = \frac{10}{9}x^{-\frac{7}{3}}; \; y^{(iv)} = -\frac{70}{27}x^{-\frac{10}{3}}$$

71. Given $f(x) - 5x^3 - 4x^2 + 8x + 9$, evaluate $f''(x)$ when the slope of the tangent line to the graph of $f(x)$ is 8.

Answer: $f''(0) = -8; f''\left(\frac{8}{15}\right) = 8$

72. For $f(x) = \sqrt{2x}$, find $f''(x)$.

a) $-\dfrac{1}{4\sqrt{2x}}$ b) $-\dfrac{1}{8x\sqrt{2x}}$ c) $-\dfrac{1}{4x\sqrt{2x}}$ d) $-\dfrac{1}{2x\sqrt{2x}}$ e) None of the above

Answer: $-\dfrac{1}{2x\sqrt{2x}}$

73. For $f(x) = \sqrt{5-x}$, find $f''(x)$.

a) $\dfrac{1}{4(5-x)^{\frac{3}{2}}}$ b) $-\dfrac{1}{2(5-x)^{\frac{3}{2}}}$ c) $-\dfrac{1}{4(5-x)^{\frac{3}{2}}}$ d) $-\dfrac{1}{2(5-x)^{\frac{1}{2}}}$ e) None of the above

Answer: $-\dfrac{1}{4(5-x)^{\frac{3}{2}}}$

74. For $f(x) = \dfrac{1}{\sqrt{2x+1}}$, find $f''(0)$.

Answer: 3

75. For $f(x) = \sqrt{x+4}$, find $f''(0)$.

Answer: $-\dfrac{1}{32}$

76. Let $y = \dfrac{2}{\sqrt{x}}$.

A. Find $\dfrac{dy}{dx}$.

Answer: $-\dfrac{1}{x\sqrt{x}}$

B. Find $\dfrac{d^2y}{dx^2}$.

Answer: $\dfrac{3}{2x^2\sqrt{x}}$

C. Find $\dfrac{d^3y}{dx^3}$.

Answer: $-\dfrac{15}{4x^3\sqrt{x}}$

77. Let $y = x^2 - \dfrac{1}{x^2}$.

A. Find $\dfrac{dy}{dx}$.

Answer: $2x + \dfrac{2}{x^3}$

B. Find $\dfrac{d^2y}{dx^2}$.

Answer: $2 - \dfrac{6}{x^4}$

C. Find $\dfrac{d^3y}{dx^3}$.

Answer: $\dfrac{24}{x^5}$

78. Find all derivatives of $y = x^5 - 2x^4 + 5x^3 - 10x^2 + 25x - 1000$.

Answer: $y' = 5x^4 - 8x^3 + 15x^2 - 20x + 25$; $y'' = 20x^3 - 24x^2 + 30x - 20$; $y''' = 60x^2 - 48x + 30$; $y^{(iv)} = 120x - 48$; $y^{(v)} = 120$; all the rest are zero

79. Find all derivatives of $y = 3x^4 - 4x^3 - 12x^2 + 13$.

Answer: $y' = 12x^3 - 12x^2 - 24x$; $y'' = 36x^2 - 24x$; $y''' = 72x - 24$; $y^{(iv)} = 72$; all the rest are zero

80. Find $\dfrac{dy}{dx}$ for $x^2 + y^2 = 4x$.

a) $\dfrac{4-x}{y}$ b) $\dfrac{x}{y}$ c) $\dfrac{2}{x+y}$ d) $\dfrac{2-x}{y}$ e) None of the above

Answer: $\dfrac{2-x}{y}$

81. Find $\dfrac{dy}{dx}$ for $x^2 - 3y^3 = 3x$.

a) $33 - 2x + 9y^2$ b) $\dfrac{3-2x}{9y}$ c) $\dfrac{2x-3}{9y^2}$ d) $\dfrac{2x-9y}{3}$ e) None of the above

Answer: $\dfrac{2x-3}{9y^2}$

82. The equation of the unit circle is given by $x^2 + y^2 = 1$. Find the equation of the tangent line drawn to the point $\left(\dfrac{\sqrt{2}}{2}, \dfrac{\sqrt{2}}{2} \right)$.

Answer: $y = -x + \sqrt{2}$

83. The equation of the unit circle is given by $x^2 + y^2 = 1$. Find the equation of the tangent line drawn to the point $\left(\dfrac{-\sqrt{2}}{2}, \dfrac{\sqrt{2}}{2} \right)$.

Answer: $y = x + \sqrt{2}$

84. A spherical hot air balloon is being filled. If the volume of the balloon is increasing at a rate of 40 ft^3/sec, at what rate is the radius increasing when the radius is 10 ft?

Answer: $\dfrac{1}{10}\pi$ ft/sec

85. Find $\dfrac{dy}{dx}$ by using implicit differentiation: $y^2 = 3x - 1$.

Answer: $\dfrac{3}{2y}$

86. Find $\dfrac{dy}{dx}$ by using implicit differentiation: $x^2 + y^2 = 1$.

Answer: $\dfrac{-x}{y}$

87. Find $\dfrac{dy}{dx}$ if $x^4 - 3y^2 + x - 10 = 0$.

Answer: $\dfrac{4x^3 + 1}{6y}$

88. Find $\dfrac{dy}{dx}$ if $5x^7 y^3 = 40$.

Answer: $\dfrac{-7y}{3x}$

89. Find $\dfrac{dy}{dx}$ if $\dfrac{(x-2)^2}{4} + .\dfrac{(y+3)^2}{9} = 1$

Answer: $\dfrac{-9(x-2)}{4(y+3)}$

90. Find $\frac{dy}{dx}$ if $x^2 - xy + y^2 = 4$.

    Answer: $\frac{2x-y}{x-2y}$

91. Find $\frac{dy}{dx}$ if $(3x+4)^2 - (2y+3)^2 = 20$

    Answer: $\frac{3(3x+4)}{2(2y+4)}$

92. Find the slope of the line tangent tot he curve $x^2 - 2xy + y^2 = 1$ at $(1,2)$.

    Answer: 1

93. Find the slope of the line tangent to the curve $(3x+4)^2 - (2y+3)^2 = 20$ at $(2,3)$.

    Answer: $\frac{5}{3}$

94. Fine the slope of the line tangent to the curve $\frac{(x-2)^2}{4} + \frac{(y+3)^2}{9} = 1$ at $(1,2)$.

    Answer: 0

95. Find the general form of the equation of the line tangent to the curve $x^2 - 2xy + y^2 = 1$ at $(1,2)$.

    Answer: $x - y + 1 = 0$

96. Find the general form of the equation of the line tangent to the curve $\frac{(x-2)^2}{4} + \frac{(y+3)^2}{9} = 1$ at $(2,0)$.

    Answer: $y = 0$

97. Find the general form of the equation of the line tangent to the curve $(3x+4)^2 - (2y+3)^2 = 20$ at $(2,3)$.

   Answer: $5x - 3y - 1 = 0$

98. Find $\dfrac{dy}{dt}$ where $xy = 16$ and $\dfrac{dx}{dt} = -2$ when $x = 1$.

   Answer: 32

99. Find $\dfrac{dx}{dt}$ where $9x^2 + 4y^2 = 144$ and $\dfrac{dy}{dt} = \sqrt{3}$ when $x = 2$ and y is positive.

   Answer: -2

100. Find $\dfrac{dy}{dt}$ where $x^2 + 4xy + 4y^2 = 1$ and $\dfrac{dx}{dt} = 5$ when $x = 4$.

   Answer: -2.5

101. Suppose that the cost (in dollars) of manufacturing x items is approximated by the formula $C(x) = 1000 + 5x + .001x^2$. Find the daily rate of change in this cost function at the time when the production level is 50 items and changing at the rate of 2 items per Day.

   Answer: $10.20

102. The annual pollution (in tons) is a function of the population (n persons, in thousands) and is modeled by the equation $P(n) = 250n$. If the population at time t (in years) is given by the formula $n(t) = \dfrac{5t-1}{3+t}$, find the rate of change in pollution at time $t = 2$.

   Answer: 160

103. Find the differential of $f(x) = 15x\sqrt{x+1}$ when $x = 0$.

   Answer: $dy = 15dx$

104. Approximate $\sqrt[3]{28}$ using differentials.

Answer: $\frac{82}{27} \approx 3.037037$

105. Approximate $\sqrt[3]{65}$ using differentials.

Answer: $\frac{193}{487} \approx 4.0208333$

106. Let t change from 3 to 3.1 for $s = t^2$.

A. Find the actual change in s.

Answer: 0.61

B. Find the approximate change in s, dt.

Answer: 0.6

107. Find the differential of y : $y = 2 - 3x^2$.

Answer: $-6x\,dx$

108. Find dy if $y = 3(x+2)^4$.

Answer: $12(x+2)^3\,dx$

109. Find dy if $y = \frac{2x+3}{4-x}$.

Answer: $11(4-x)^{-2}\,dx$

110. Find dy if $y = 5x - \frac{x^2}{200} - 1550$.

Answer: $\left(5 - \frac{x}{100}\right)^{-2}\,dx$

111. Find dy if $y = 5\sqrt[3]{x^3 - 4}$.

Answer: $\frac{15}{2}x^2(x^3-4)^{-\frac{1}{2}}dx$

112. Find dy if $y = (2x-4)^2(5-x)^2$.

Answer: $4(x-2)(5-x)^2(16-5x)dx$

113. Find dy and Δy for $y = 3x^2$, $x = 10$, $\Delta x = 0.1$.

Answer: $\Delta y = 6.03$; $dy = 6$

114. Find dy and Δy for $y = 3x^2 - 4x + 5$ when $x = 5$ and $\Delta x = 0.1$.

Answer: $\Delta y = 2.63$; $dy = 2.6$

115. Find dy and Δy for $y = \frac{2x-1}{x+2}$ when $x = 10$ and $\Delta x = 0.1$.

Answer: $\Delta y \approx 0.003444$; $dy \approx 0.003472$

116. Find dy and Δy for $y = \frac{x^2+x-6}{x+5x+6}$ when $x = 2$ and $\Delta x = 0.1$.

Answer: $\Delta y \approx 0.02439$; $dy = 0.025$

117. Find dy and Δy for $y = 3\sqrt{2x}$ when $x = 8$ and $\Delta x = 0.2$.

Answer: $\Delta y \approx 0.14907$; $dy = 0.15$

118. If $y = \sqrt[3]{x}$, estimate the change in y when $x = 8$ for a change in x of -0.02.

Answer: -0.00166667

119. If $y = \sqrt[4]{x}$, estimate the change in y when $x = 16$ for a change in x of 0.15.

Answer: 0.0046875

120. If $y = \frac{4}{3}\pi x^3$, estimate the change in y when $x = 12$ for a change in x of 0.2.

Answer: 80π

121. If $y = 3(100 - x^{-3})$, estimate the change in y when $x = 10$ and $\Delta x = 0.02$.

Answer: 0.000018

122. If $y = \frac{x-1}{\sqrt{x^2+21}}$, estimate the change in y when $x = 10$ and $\Delta x = 2$.

Answer: -0.088655146

123. Let $f(x) = (x^3 + 7)^{\frac{1}{2}}$ and $g(x) = (3x^2 + 1)^3$.

A. Find $\frac{d}{dx}(f(x) + g(x))$.

Answer: $\frac{3}{2}x^2(x^3 + 7)^{\frac{-1}{2}} + 18x(3x^2 + 1)^2$

B. Find $\frac{d}{dx}(f(x)g(x))$.

Answer: $\frac{3}{2}x^2(x^3 + 7)^{\frac{-1}{2}}(3x^2 + 1)^3 + 18x(3x^2 + 1)^2(x^3 + 7)^{\frac{1}{2}}$

C. Find $\frac{d}{dx}\left(\frac{f(x)}{g(x)}\right)$.

Answer: $\dfrac{\frac{3}{2}x^2(x^3+7)^{\frac{-1}{2}}(3x^2+1)+18x(x^3+7)^{\frac{1}{2}}}{(3x^2+1)^4}$

124. Let $f(x) = g'(x)$, $g(x) = h'(x)$, and $h(x) = 2x^2 + 3x + 1$.

A. Find $f'(x)$ at $x = 2$.

Answer: $f'(2) = 0$

B. If $k(x) = f'(x)$, what is $k'(x)$?

Answer: $k'(x) = 0$

125. Let $g(x) = \dfrac{[f(x)]^{(m+1)}}{m+1}$. Find $g'(x)$.

Answer: $[f(x)]^m f'(x)$

126. Let $y = v^3$, $v = u^{\frac{1}{2}}$, and $u = \frac{1}{x}$. Find $\dfrac{dy}{dx}$ by the Chain Rule.

Answer: $\dfrac{dy}{dx} = \dfrac{-3}{2} x^{\frac{-5}{2}}$

127. Let $f(x) = x^c$. Find $f^{(5)}(x)$. Use the result to find $g^{(5)}(x)$
if $g(x) = x^5 + x^4 + x^3 + x^2 + x$.

Answer: $f^{(5)}(x) = c(c-1)(c-2)(c-3)(c-4)x^{c-5}$; $g^{(5)}(x) = 120$

128. Find y''' for $y = x^3 + x^{\frac{5}{2}}$ at $x = 0$.

Answer: y''' does not exist at $x = 0$.

129. Find $\dfrac{dy}{dx}$ for $x^2 + 3y = y^2 + xy$.

Answer: $y' = \dfrac{2x-y}{2y+x-3}$

130. Let $y = 2\sqrt{3x} + x^2$.

A. Find the differential dy.

Answer: $dy = \left(\dfrac{3}{\sqrt{3x}} + 2x \right) dx$

B. Use *dy* to approximate Δy when *x* changes from 3 to 3.01.

Answer: 0.07

131. Use differentials to approximate $\sqrt{0.1}$

Answer: $\dfrac{17}{54}$

APPLIED CALCULUS

CHAPTER 4
APPLICATIONS OF THE DERIVATIVE

1. Find the interval(s) where $f(x) = x^3 - 6x^2 + 9x + 25$ is increasing and where it is decreasing, if any.

    Answer: Increasing on $(-\infty, 1) \cup (3, \infty)$; decreasing on $(1, 3)$.

2. For what value(s) is the function $f(x) = 2x^3 - 12x^2 + 18x + 1$ increasing?

    a) all x b) $1 < x < 3$ c) $x < 1$

    d) $x < 1,\ x > 3$ e) Function is never increasing

    Answer: $x < 1,\ x > 3$

3. Find the interval(s) on which $y = \frac{x}{x-4}$ is increasing and the interval(s) where it is decreasing.

    Answer: Decreasing on $(-\infty, 4) \cup (4, \infty)$; never increasing

4. Find the interval(s) on which $y = x^3 - 3x$ is increasing and the interval(s) where it is decreasing.

    Answer: Increasing on $(-\infty, -1) \cup (1, \infty)$; decreasing $(-1, 1)$

5. Use the Second Derivative Test to find the relative extrema of
$f(x) = 3x^4 - 8x^3 - 18x^2 + 14$.

Answer: Relative minima: $(-1, 7)$, $(3, -121)$; relative maxima: $(0, 14)$

6. If $f'(c) = 0$, then c is a critical point.

a) True   b) False

Answer: True

7. If c is a critical point of f, then $f''(c) = 0$.

a) True   b) False

Answer: False

8. How many critical points does $y = \sqrt{x+1} + (2x+1)^5$ have?

a) None   b) 1   c) 2   d) 3   e) 4

Answer: 1

9. How many critical points does $y = \sqrt{x} + x^3$ have?

a) None   b) 1   c) 2   d) 3   e) 4

Answer: 1

10. If f has a relative maximum at $x = c$, then $f'(c) = 0$.

   a) True   b) False

   Answer: False

11. Consider $y = \sqrt[3]{x}$. The point $(0, 0)$ is:

   a) a relative minimum   b) an absolute minimum   c) a local maximum
   d) an absolute maximum   e) none of the above

   Answer: None of the above

12. If $f(1) = 3$, $f'(1) = 0$, and $f''(1) = 6$, then $(1, 3)$ must be:

   a) a relative minimum   b) a relative maximum   c) a point of inflection
   d) an absolute minimum   e) none of the above

   Answer: a relative minimum

13. If $f(2) = 3$, $f'(2) = 0$, and $f''(2) = -6$, then which of the following points must be a relative maximum?

   a) $(2, 0)$ b) $(2, -6)$
   c) $(3, -6)$ d) $(2, 3)$
   e) Insufficient information to give answer

   Answer: $(2, 3)$

14. Use the First Derivative Test to find the relative maximum and minimum points for the function $f(x) = x^3 - 3x$.

   Answer: $(1, -2)$ is a relative minimum; $(-1, 2)$ is a relative maximum

15. Use the First Derivative Test to find the relative maximum and minimum points for the function $f(x) = x^4 - x^2$.

   Answer: $\left(\pm\sqrt{\frac{1}{2}}, -\frac{1}{4} \right)$ are relative minima; $(0, 0)$ is a relative maximum

16. Find the relative maxima and minima for $f(x) = x^3 - x^2 - 5x + 6$.

   Answer: Relative minimum at $x = \frac{5}{3}$ and a relative maximum at $x = -1$

17. Find the relative maxima and mimima for $f(x) = x + 3x^{-1}$.

   Answer: Relative minimum at $x = \sqrt{3}$ and a relative maximum at $x = -\sqrt{3}$

18. Find the relative maxima and minima for $f(x) = \frac{1}{2}x^4 - 2x^3 - 88x^2 + 498x$.

   Answer: Relative minima at $x = \pm 2\sqrt{22}$ and relative maximum at $x = 3$

19. Find the relative maxima and minima for $f(x) = 4 + 18x^2 - x^4$.

   Answer: Relative maxima at $x = \pm 3$ and the relative minimum at $x = 0$

20. Find the relative maxima and minima for $f(x) = 3x^4 - 4x^3 - 12x^2 + 13$.

   Answer: Relative minimum at $x = -1$ and relative maximum at $x = 0$

70

21. Let $f(x) = \frac{x}{9x^2-100}$.

A. Determine where $f(x)$ is concave upward.

Answer: $\left(-\frac{10}{3},0\right)\cup\left(\frac{10}{3},\infty\right)$

B. Determine where $f(x)$ is concave downward.

Answer: $\left(-\infty,-\frac{10}{3}\right)\cup\left(0,\frac{10}{3}\right)$

C. Determine any inflection points of $f(x)$

Answer: $(0,0)$

22. Find all asymptotes, vertical and horizontal, for the graph of $f(x) = \frac{5x^2-39x-8}{x^2-x-12}$.

Answer: Horizontal asymptote: $y=5$; vertical asymptote: $x=4$, $x=-3$

23. Determine the symmetry, if any, and graph $f(x) = \frac{6x^2}{x^2+25}$

Answer: y-axis symmetry

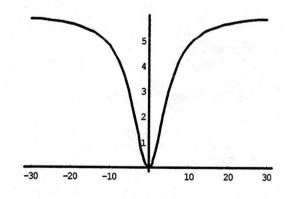

24. Graph $f(x) = \frac{8x}{x^2+7}$ and identify the absolut extrema, if any.

Answer: Absolute minimum: $\left(-\sqrt{7}, \frac{-4\sqrt{7}}{7}\right)$; absolute maximum: $\left(\sqrt{7}, \frac{4\sqrt{7}}{7}\right)$

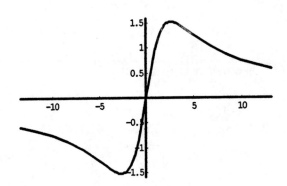

25. Graph $f(x) = 25x^3 - 30x^2 + 9x$ over the interval $[-1, 3]$ and identify the absolute extrema.

Answer: Absolute minimum: $(-1, -64)$; absolute maximum: $(3, 432)$

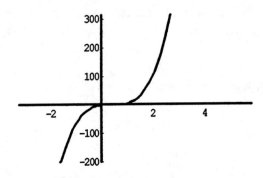

26. If $(c, f(c))$ is a point of inflection, then $f''(c) = 0$.

a) True   b) False

Answer: True

72

27. Consider $f(x) = x^3 - 12x^2 - 8$. Find the point(s) of inflection.

   a) $(0, -8)$ and $(8, -264)$ b) $(6, -224)$ c) $(4, -136)$
   d) $(0, -8)$ and $(6, 224)$ e) No points of inflection

   <u>Answer:</u> $(4, -136)$

28. Find the points of inflection for the function $g(x) = x^4 - 6x^2$.

   <u>Answer:</u> $(1, -5)$ and $(-1, -5)$

29. Sketch the graph of $y = -x^3 + 3x^2 + 24x - 72$.

   <u>Answer:</u>

   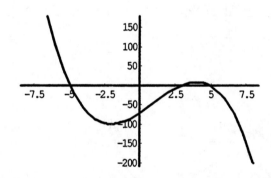

30. Sketch the graph of $y = x^3 - \frac{5}{2}x^2 - 2x + \frac{1}{2}$.

   <u>Answer:</u>

   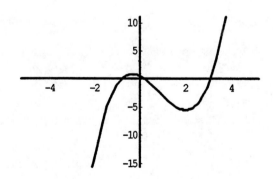

31. Sketch the graph of $y = x + \frac{1}{x}$.

Answer:

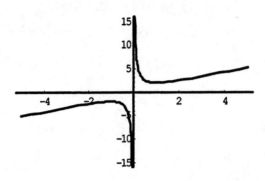

32. Graph $y = 2x^3 + 9x^2 - 60x + 8$ by finding the critical values, determining when it is increasing and when it is decreasing, and by deciding upon the concavity.

Answer: Critical values: $x = -5, 2$; relative maximum at $x = -5$; relative minimum at $x = 2$; concave down on $\left(-\infty, \frac{3}{2}\right)$; concave up on $\left(-\frac{3}{2}, \infty\right)$

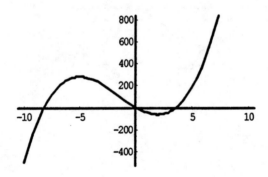

33. Graph $y = x^4 - 18x^2 + 5$ by finding the critical values, determining when it is increasing and when it is decreasing, and by deciding upon the concavity.

Answer: Critical values: $x = 0, 3, -3$; relative maximum at $x = 0$; relative minimum at $x = 3$ and $x = -3$; concave down on $(-\sqrt{3}, \sqrt{3})$; concave up on $(-\infty, -\sqrt{3}) \cup (\sqrt{3}, \infty)$

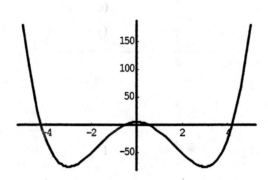

34. Graph $y = x^3 - x^2 - 8x + 12$ by finding the critical values, determining when it is increasing and when it is decreasing, and by deciding upon the concavity.

Answer: Critical values: $x = -\frac{4}{3}, 2$; relative maximum at $x = -\frac{4}{3}$; relative minimum at $x = 2$; concave down on $\left(-\infty, \frac{1}{3}\right)$; concave up on $\left(\frac{1}{3}, \infty\right)$

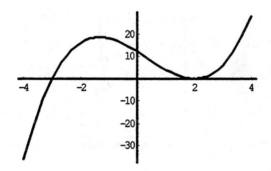

35. Graph $y = 3x^3 - 4x^2 + 8x - 9$ by finding the critical values, determining when it is increasing and when it is decreasing, and by deciding upon the concavity.

Answer: Critical values: *None*; concave down on $\left(-\infty, \frac{4}{9}\right)$; concave up on $\left(\frac{4}{9}, \infty\right)$

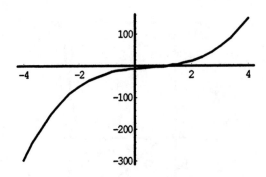

36. Graph $y = 3x^4 - 4x^3 - 12x^2 + 13$ by finding the critical values, determining when it is increasing and when it is decreasing, and by deciding upon the concavity.

Answer: Critical values: $x = -1, 0, 2$; relative maximum at $x = 0$; relative minimum at $x = -1$ and $x = 2$; concave down on $\left(\frac{1-\sqrt{7}}{3}, \frac{1+\sqrt{7}}{3}\right)$; concave up on $\left(-\infty, \frac{1-\sqrt{7}}{3}\right) \cup \left(\frac{1+\sqrt{7}}{3}, \infty\right)$

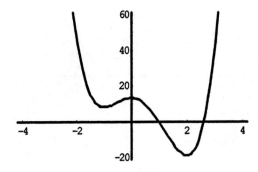

37.   Graph $f(x) = 4x^3 - 12x^2 + 12x + 75$

Answer:

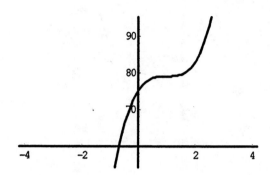

38.   Graph $y = \frac{x^2+3}{x}$

Answer:

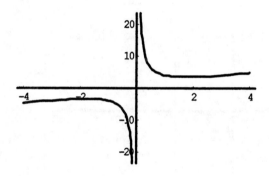

39.   Graph $f(x) = x^4 - 1$

Answer:

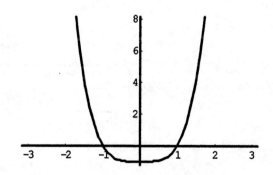

40. Graph $f(x) = (x-1)^3 + 2$

Answer:

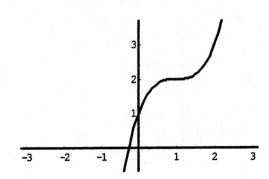

41. Graph $y = \frac{x-3}{x+2}$

Answer:

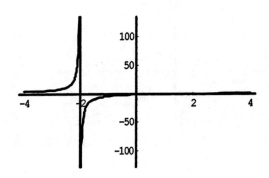

42. Determine any horizontal asymptotes for $y = \frac{3x-1}{x+1}$

Answer: $y = 3$

43. Determine any horizontal or vertical asymptotes for $y = \frac{3x}{x^2-2}$

Answer: $y = 0, \ x = \pm\sqrt{2}$

44.   A dairy farmer recently acquired a large tract of land adjoining his property. He intends
        to fence off a 3000 square yard rectangular feed lot. Local codes require that he build
        a fence along the side of the lot along the country road. This fence can be built with
        material costing $19 per running yard. The other three sides of the lot can be fenced at
        A cost of $9 per yard. Find the dimensions of the lot that will minimize the fencing
        cost.

        Answer: Along road (and parallel side): $\frac{30\sqrt{105}}{7}$ yards
                 Other two sides: $\frac{20\sqrt{105}}{3}$ yards

45.   Let $y = \frac{x^2+1}{x}$ on the interval [0.5,10].

A.   What is the absolute minimum value of the function on the given interval?

        Answer: 2

B.   Graph the function.

        Answer:

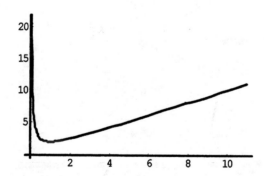

C.   Why is there no absolute minimum value of the function on the interval $[-10, 10]$?

        Answer: $y \to -\infty$ as $x \to 0^-$

46. A company has determined that the relationship between the quantity of an item sold (x) and the asking price (p) in dollars is: $p = 50 - \frac{x}{8}$, $0 \le x \le 360$.

A. Determine the revenue equation.

Answer: $50x - \frac{x^2}{8}$

B. For what value(s) of x is revenue increasing?

Answer: $0 < x < 200$

C. For what value(s) of x is revenue decreasing?

Answer: $200 < x < 360$

D. What asking price will produce the maximum revenue?

Answer: $25

E. What is the maximum revenue?

Answer: $5000

47. A company has determined that the relationship between the quantity of an item sold (x) and the asking price (p) in dollars is: $p = 125 - \frac{x}{4}$, $0 \le x \le 400$.

A. Determine the revenue equation.

Answer: $125x - \frac{x^2}{4}$

B. For what value(s) of x is revenue increasing?

Answer: $0 < x < 250$

C. For what value(s) of x is revenue decreasing?

Answer: $250 < x < 400$

D. What asking price will produce the maximum revenue?

Answer: $62.50

E. What is the maximum revenue?

Answer: $15,625

48. A company has determined that its profit P depends upon the amount of money spent on advertising, x. The relationship is given by the equation $P(x) = \frac{2x}{x^2+4} + 70$, where P and x are measured in thousands of dollars.

A. What amount should the company spend on advertising to assure maximum profit?

Answer: $2000

81

B.   What is the profit?

Answer: $70,500

49.   Consider the relationship between profit P and selling price s (each measured in dollars): $P = 10,000s - 100s^2$.

A.   Is the profit increasing or decreasing when the selling price is $40.00?

Answer: increasing

B.   For what range of selling prices is profit increasing?

Answer: $0 < s < 50$

C.   What selling price results in maximum profit?

Answer: $50.00

50.   Suppose that the relationship between profit P and selling price s (each measured in dollars): $P = 40,000s - 200s^2$.

A.   Is the profit increasing or decreasing when the selling price is $80.00?

Answer: increasing

B.   For what range of selling prices is profit increasing?

Answer: $0 < s < 100$

C.   What selling price results in maximum profit?

       Answer: $100.00

51.   A firm has determined that it revenue $R(x)$ (measured in thousands of dollars) from the sale of x units of its product is: $R(x) = 80 - \dfrac{200}{x+4} - 2x.$

A.   Find the value of x that maximizes revenue.

       Answer: 6

B.   Find the maximum revenue.

       Answer: $48,000

52.   Find the absolute maximum and minimum for $y = (x+4)(x-2)^2$ on $[-5, 5]$.

       Answer: Maximum at $x = 5$; minimum at $x = -5$

53.   Find the absolute maximum and minimum for $f(x) = 3\sqrt{x+x}$ on $[0, 4]$.

       Answer: Maximum at $x = 4$; minimum at $x = 0$

54.   Find the absolute maximum and minimum for $y = 1 - x^{\frac{5}{3}}$ on $[0, 8]$.

       Answer: Maximum at $x = 0$; minimum at $x = 8$.

55. Find the absolute maximum and minimum for $f(x) = 2x^3 + 5x^2 + 4x - 6$ on $[-2, 0]$.

Answer: Maximum at $x = 0$; minimum at $x = -2$

56. Find the maximum profit when it is known that the revenue and cost functions are $R(x) = 500x + 70.5x^2 - x^3$ and $C(x) = 1000 + 50x$.

Answer: $72,750

57. Find the maximum profit when it is known that the revenue and cost functions are $R(x) = 20x - \dfrac{2x}{x-150}$ and $C(x) = 2000 + 5x$.

Answer: $330.50 when $x = 158$

58. A property management company manages 200 apartments renting for $800 with all the apartments rented. For each $50 per month increase in rent there will be two vacancies with no possibility of filling them. What rent per apartment will maximize the monthly Revenue?

Answer: $2900

59. The price of a certain stock at time t $(0 \le t \le 5)$ is estimated by $P(t) = 0.1t^3 + 0.05t^2 - 3t + 10$. When will the stock price be a maximum, when will it reach a minimum?

Answer: Maximum price at hour 0 and minimum price at hour 3.

84

60. The mosquito population is a function of rainfall, and can be approximated by the formula $N(x) = 1000 + 30x + 44.5x^2 - x^3$, where x is the number of inches of rainfall. When will the population be a maximum?

Answer: $x = 30$ inches

61. What are the dimensions of the largest right circular cylinder that can be inscribed in a sphere of radius 10 in.?

Answer: radius $= \dfrac{10\sqrt{6}}{3}$ in.; $h = \dfrac{20\sqrt{3}}{3}$ in.

62. Find the intervals where $f(x) = \dfrac{x^2-9}{x^2-1}$ is increasing and where $f(x)$ is decreasing.

Answer: Decreasing on $(-\infty, -1) \cup (-1, 0)$
            Increasing on $(0, 1) \cup (1, \infty)$

63. Find the intervals where $f(x) = 6x - 3x^2$ is increasing and where $f(x)$ is decreasing.

Answer: Increasing on $(-\infty, 1)$
            Decreasing on $(1, \infty)$

64. Use the First Derivative Test to determine the relative extrema of $f(x) = \dfrac{x^2-1}{x^2}$.

Answer: None

65. Use the First Derivative Test to determine the relative extrema of $f(x) = \sqrt{x^2-1} + x$.

Answer: None

66. What are the critical values of $g(x) = 4x^5 + 5x^4$?

Answer: $x = 0, -1$

67. Determine if $f(x)$ is concave up or concave down on the interval $(-1, 2)$ if $f'(x) = 3x^2 + 6x + 2$.

Answer: Concave up

68. For $f(x) = x^3 + 3x + 1$ determine the intervals of concavity.

Answer: Concave down on $(-\infty, 0)$; concave up on $(0, \infty)$

69. Let $h(x) = x^{\frac{1}{7}}$. Find all points of inflection.

Answer: $(0, 0)$

70. Use the Second Derivative Test to determine the relative extrema of $g(x) = \frac{x^2+1}{x^2-1}$.

Answer: Relative minimum at $x = 0$

71. Use the Second Derivative Test to determine where $f(x) = \frac{4}{x^3-1}$ is concave up and concave down.

Answer: Concave down on $(-\infty, -1) \cup (0, 1)$
Concave up on $(-1, 0) \cup (1, \infty)$

72. If $f''(c) = 0$, then which of the following are always true?

    a) $f'(x)$ is constant at $x = c$
    b) $f(x)$ must have a relative extreme at $x = c$
    c) $f(c)$ is an inflection point
    d) None of the above

    <u>Answer:</u> None of the above

73. Determine if the following functions are either not symmetric, symmetric about the y-axis or symmetric about the origin.

A) $f(x) = x^2 + 1$

    <u>Answer:</u> Symmetric about y-axis

B) $f(x) = \frac{x^2 + 4}{x^2 - 4}$

    <u>Answer:</u> Symmetric about y-axis

C) $f(x) = x^2(x + 1)(x - 1)$

    <u>Answer:</u> Symmetric about y-axis

D) $f(x) = 3x^7 - x^5 + x^3 - 3x + 1$

    <u>Answer:</u> Not symmetric

E) $f(x) = 5$

Answer: Symmetric about y-axis

F) $f(x) = x$

Answer: Symmetric about the origin

74. Determine the vertical asymptotes of the functions below:

A. $f(x) = \frac{x^2 - 9}{x + 3}$

Answer: No asymptotes

B. $f(x) = \frac{x^3 - 1}{x + 2}$

Answer: $x = 2$

75. Determine the horizontal asymptote(s) of $f(x) = -6x^{-7}$

Answer: $y = 0$

76. Find the absolute extrema for $g(x) = 2x - 5x^{\frac{4}{5}}$ on the interval $[-1, 3]$.

Answer: Absolute maximum at $(0, 0)$; absolute minimum at $(4, -7)$

APPLIED CALCULUS

CHAPTER 5
EXPONENTIAL AND LOGARITHMIC FUNCTIONS

1. On a production line, the number of units (y) assembled each day, x days after the production run began is given by: $y = 100\left(1 - e^{-0.3x}\right)$.

A. What is the level of production after 5 days?

   Answer: 77.7 units

B. What is the level of production after 20 days?

   Answer: 99.8 units

2. Solve for x: $e^{3x-1} = 5$.

   a) $\frac{1}{3}\ln 6$ b) $\frac{1}{3} + \frac{1}{3}\ln 5$ c) $\frac{1}{3}\ln 5$ d) $\frac{-1}{3} - \frac{1}{3}\ln 5$ e) None of the above

   Answer: $\frac{1}{3} + \frac{1}{3}\ln 5$

3. Solve for x: $e^{3x+6} = 9$.

   a) $\frac{1}{3}\ln 3$ b) $\ln 3 - 2$ c) $\frac{1}{3}(-6 + \ln 9)$ d) 1   e) None of the above

   Answer: $\frac{1}{3}(-6 + \ln 9)$

4. Solve for x: $7e^{1-x} = 10$.

   Answer: $1 - \ln 10 + \ln 7 \approx 0.6433$

5. Solve for x: $3e^{2-3x} = 19$.

   Answer: $\frac{1}{3}(2 - \ln 19 + \ln 3) \approx 0.0514$

6. Simplify: $81^{\frac{3}{4}}$

   Answer: 27

7. Simplify: $\dfrac{32^{\frac{2}{5}}}{32^{\frac{1}{2}}}$

   Answer: $2^{-\frac{1}{2}}$

8. Simplify: $\dfrac{\left(2^{\frac{1}{3}}\right)^{6}}{8^{\frac{2}{3}}}$

   Answer: 1

9. Simplify: $x^{\frac{1}{3}}\left(x^{\frac{2}{3}}-x^{-\frac{1}{3}}\right)$

   Answer: $x-1$

10. Simplify: $x^{\frac{2}{3}}\left(x^{\frac{1}{6}}+x^{-\frac{1}{2}}\right)$

    Answer: $x^{\frac{5}{6}}+x^{\frac{1}{6}}$

11. Graph $y=3^{-x}$.

    Answer:

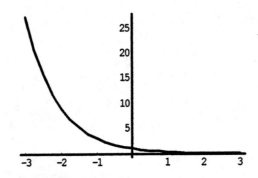

90

12. Graph $f(x) = -\left(\frac{1}{3}\right)^x$.

Answer:

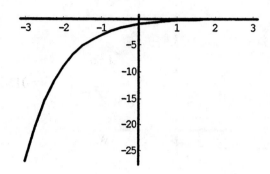

13. Graph $y = e^{2x}$.

Answer:

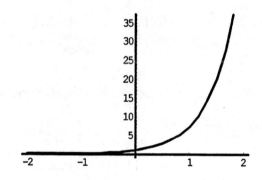

14. Graph $f(x) = -3^{2x}$.

Answer:

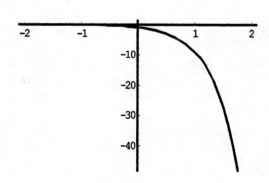

15. Graph $y = e^{x-1} - 1$.

    Answer:

    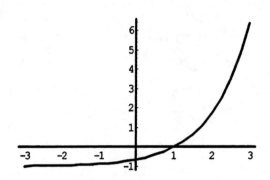

16. Solve for x: $10^{2x-1} = 6$ (do not approximate your answer).

    Answer: $\dfrac{\log 6 + 1}{2}$

17. Solve for x: $3^{x^2 - 2x} = 27$

    Answer: $3, -1$

18. Solve for x: $e^x + 8e^{-x} - 6 = 0$

    Answer: $\ln 2, \ln 4$

19. Solve for x: $10^{2x^2 + x} = 1000$

    Answer: $-\dfrac{3}{2}, 1$

20. Write $\log 10 = 1$ in exponential form.

    Answer: $10^1 = 10$

21. Find the exponential equivalent of $\log_x Y = Z$.

    a) $XY = Z$ b) $X^Z = Y$ c) $Y^X = Z$ d) $Z^X = Y$ e) None of the above

    Answer: $X^Z = Y$

92

22. Find the logarithmic equivalent of $X^Y = Z$.

a) $\log_X Z = Y$ b) $Y \log X = Z$ c) $\log_X Y = Z$ d) $\log_Y Z = X$ e) None of the above

Answer: $\log_X Z = Y$

23. Solve for x: $\log_2 \frac{1}{\sqrt[3]{x}} = 1$.

a) $\frac{1}{8}$ b) 3   c) 1   d) −8   e) None of the above

Answer: $\frac{1}{8}$

24. Solve for x: $\log_3 \sqrt{x} = 1$.

a) $\frac{1}{3}$ b) 3   c) 9   d) 0   e) None of the above

Answer: 9

25. Which of the following is a sketch of $y = \log_2 (x+1)$?

a)

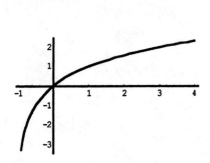

b)

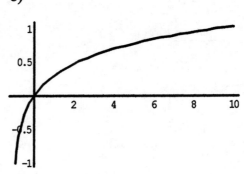

c)

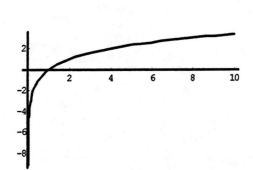

d)

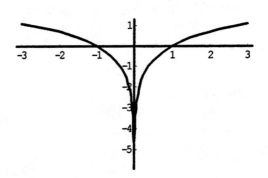

e) None of the above

Answer: a)

26. Which of the following is a sketch of $y = \ln|x|$?

a)

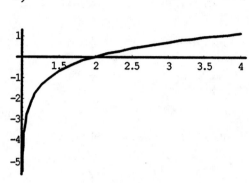

b)

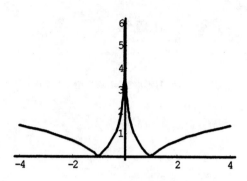

c)

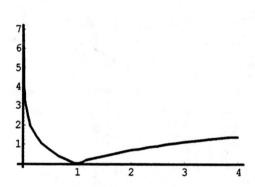

d)

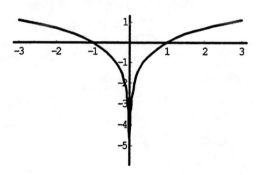

e) None of the above

Answer: d)

95

27. The demand function for a product is described by: $p = \dfrac{300}{\ln(x+4)}$, where x represents the number of units demanded at price p.

A. Determine the price when 5 units are demanded.

   Answer: $136.54

B. Determine the price when 30 units are demanded.

   Answer: $85.07

28. Graph $y = \log_8 x$.

   Answer:

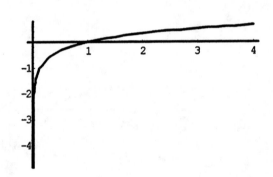

29. Graph $y = \ln x$

   Answer:

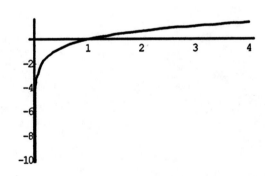

30. Graph $y = \log_\pi x$.

    Answer:

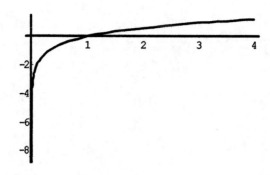

31. Graph $y = \log_{0.15} x$.

    Answer:

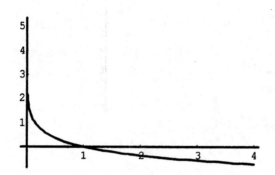

32. Graph $y = \ln(x-1) + 1$.

    Answer:

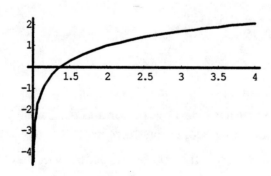

33. Solve for x : $\log x + \log(x-2) = \log 15$.

    Answer: 5

34. Solve for x: $\log_2(x-8) = 2 - \log_2(x-2)$.

   Answer: $5 + 2\sqrt{13}$

35. Solve for x: $\log\sqrt{x^2 + 199} = 2$.

   Answer: ± 99

36. Solve for x: $3\ln 5e = 3 - \ln x$.

   Answer: 5^{-3}

37. Solve for x: $\ln\sqrt[3]{x+5} = \log_2 8$.

   Answer: $e^9 - 5$

38. Solve for n: $A = P(1+i)^n$

   Answer: $\log_{(1+i)}\dfrac{A}{P}$ or $\dfrac{\log\frac{A}{P}}{\log(1+i)}$

39. The projected sales for Coke and Pepsi in a certain market are modeled by $C(t) = 4000(1.15)^{\frac{t}{10}}$ and $P(t) = 5000(0.95)^t$, where t is the number of years from 1987. When will the sales for Coke and Pepsi be the same?

   Answer: $\dfrac{\log 5 - \log 4}{\frac{1}{10}\log 1.15 - \log 0.95} \approx 3.4188$

40. Sociologists often assume that the rate at which a rumor spreads is based on the proportion of the population that has heard the rumor and the fraction of the population that has not. If $P(t)$ is the number of people that have heard the news, then $P(t) = \dfrac{1000P_0}{P_0 + (1000 - P_0)e^{-kt}}$, where P_0 is the number of people who have heard the rumor at time $t = 0$ days. Find $P(1)$ if it is known that $P_0 = 10$ and $k = 5$.

   Answer: About 598 people

41. A secretary's typing speed (in words per minute) after t years of experience can be modeled by the equation $S(t) = 90 - 32\left(\frac{1}{2}\right)^t$. How long will it take to reach a typing speed of 80 words per minute? Give both an exact answer and an answer rounded to the nearest year.

Answer: $\log_{\frac{1}{2}} \frac{5}{16} \approx 2$ years

42. Suppose the price-demand and price-supply equations for x-thousands of units of a product are given by:

Demand: $d(x) = 500e^{-.2x}$

Supply: $s(x) = 50e^{0.1x}$

Fine the equilibrium point. Give both an exact answer and an answer rounded to four decimal places.

Answer: $\frac{10}{3} \ln 10$ is Approx. 7.6753

43. Write $10^{\frac{1}{3}} = \sqrt[3]{10}$ in logarithmic form.

Answer: $\log \sqrt[3]{10} = \frac{1}{3}$

44. Write $6^0 = 1$ in logarithmic form.

Answer: $\log_6 1 = 0$

45. Write $e^{-1} = \frac{1}{e}$ in logarithmic form.

Answer: $\ln \frac{1}{e} = -1$

46. Write $5^4 = 625$ in logarithmic form.

Answer: $\log_5 625 = 4$

47. Write $81^{-\frac{3}{4}} = \frac{1}{27}$ in logarithmic form.

   Answer: $\log_{81} \frac{1}{27} = -\frac{3}{4}$

48. Write $\log_3 81 = 4$ in exponential form.

   Answer: $3^4 = 81$

49. Write $\pi = x$ in exponential form.

   Answer: $e^x = \pi$

50. Write $\ln x = 5$ in exponential form.

   Answer: $e^5 = x$

51. Write $\ln e^\pi = \pi$ exponential form.

   Answer: $e^\pi = e^\pi$

52. Find the present value of $25,000 due in 5 years at an annual rate of 7 percent compounded continuously. (Round to the nearest dollar.)

   Answer: $17,617

53. The monthly payment, P, of an amortized loan is an exponential function of the total number of payments to be made, t, and is given by the formula:

$$P = V \cdot \frac{i}{[1-(1+i)^{-t}]},$$

   where V represents the amount of the loan in dollars and i represents the interest per period (monthly).

A. Find the monthly payment on a 30 - year mortgage loan ($t = 360$) of $50,000 ($V = 50,000$) that has an annual interest rate 12% ($i = 0.01$).

   Answer: $514.31

100

B. How much interest is paid back over the life of the loan?

Answer: $135,151

54. The monthly payment, P, of an amortized loan is an exponential function of the total number of payments to be made, t, and is given by the formula:

$$P = V \cdot \frac{i}{[1-(1+i)^{-t}]},$$

where V represents the amount of the loan in dollars and i represents the interest per period (monthly).

A. Find the monthly payment on a 15- year mortgage loan ($t = 180$) of $50,000 ($V = 50,000$) that has an annual interest rate 12% ($i = 0.01$).

Answer: $600.08

B. How much interest is paid back over the life of the loan?

Answer: $58,015

55. A company has determined that the value V (in dollars) of its investments (which have grown at an annual rate of increase of 2%) is: $V = 20,000(1.02)^t$, where t is the number of years since the investments were made. Find the value of the company's investments after five years.

Answer: $22,081.62

56. A company has determined that the value V (in dollars) of its investments (which have grown at an annual rate of increase of 5%) is: $V = 10,000(1.05)^t$, where t is the number of years since the investments were made. Find the value of the company's investments after five years.

Answer: $16,288.95

57. A company has determined that the demand for x hundred units of its product, based on the price p, is: $p = 50e^{-0.04x}$.

A. Find the marginal revenue.

Answer: $50e^{-0.04x}(1 - 0.04x)$

B. How many units should the company produce and sell to maximize its revenue?

Answer: 2500

58. Find the derivative of $f(x) = \frac{9 + e^{6x}}{x}$.

Answer: $\frac{6xe^{6x} - e^{6x} - 9}{x^2}$

59. Find both the first and second derivatives of $f(x) = -5e^{2x^3}$.

Answer: $f'(x) = -30x^2 e^{2x^3}$; $f''(x) = -30xe^{2x^3}(6x^3 + 2)$

60. Graph $f(x) = xe^{-2x}$ and list any relative extrema

Answer: Relative maximum: $\left(\frac{1}{2}, \frac{1}{2e}\right)$

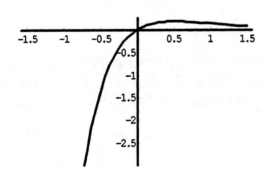

61. Find the derivative of $f(x) = x \ln 2x$.

Answer: $\ln x + \ln 2 + 1$

62. If $y = e^{x^2}$, find $\frac{dy}{dx}$.

     a) $2e^{x^2}$ b) $\frac{xe^{x^2}}{2}$ c) $2xe^{x^2}$ d) $x^2e^{x^2-1}$ e) None of the above

     Answer: $2xe^{x^2}$

63. If $f(x) = \frac{e^{3x}}{e^{3x}+1}$, find $f'(x)$.

     a) $\frac{3e^{3x}}{(e^{3x}+1)^2}$ b) $\frac{1}{(e^{3x}+1)^2}$ c) $\frac{e^{3x}}{e^{6x}+1}$ d) $\frac{3e^{6x}}{e^{6x}+1}$ e) None of the above

     Answer: $\frac{3e^{3x}}{(e^{3x}+1)^2}$

64. Find $\frac{d^2y}{dx^2}$ if $y = e^{x^2+1} + 3x$.

     Answer: $2(2x^2+1)\left(e^{x^2+1}\right)$

65. Find $\frac{d^2y}{dx^2}$ if $y = e^{x^2} + 10x$.

     Answer: $2e^{x^2}\left(2x^2+1\right)$

66. Let $f(x) = xe^{-x^2}$.

A. What are the critical points of f?

     Answer: $\frac{\sqrt{2}}{2}$ and $-\frac{\sqrt{2}}{2}$

B. What is the absolute minimum of f in the interval $-2 \le x \le 2$?

     Answer: $-\frac{1}{\sqrt{2e}}$ is approx. -0.42888

67. A company has determined that the demand for x hundred units of its product, based on the price p, is: $p = 100e^{-0.05x}$.

A. Find the marginal revenue.

Answer: $100e^{-0.05x}(1 - 0.05x)$

B. How many units should the company produce and sell to maximize its revenue?

Answer: 2000

68. Find y' when $y = x^2 e^{3x}$.

Answer: $x(3x + 2)e^{3x}$

69. Find $\frac{dy}{dx}$ for $y = \frac{1}{e^x + x^3}$.

Answer: $\frac{-(e^x + 3x^2)}{(e^x + x^3)^2}$

70. Find the derivative of $\sqrt{e^x}$.

Answer: $\frac{1}{2}e^{\frac{1}{2}x}$ or $\frac{1}{2}\sqrt{e^x}$

71. Find y' when $y = e^{x^2} + e^{x^3}$.

Answer: $2xe^{x^2} + 3x^2 e^{x^3}$

72. Find $\frac{dy}{dx}$ for $y = \frac{e^x - e^{-x}}{e^x + e^{-x}}$.

Answer: $\frac{4}{(e^x + e^{-x})^2}$

73. Find the derivative of $f(x) = \ln(e^{5x} + 7)$.

   Answer: $\dfrac{5e^{5x}}{e^{5x}+7}$

74. Let $f(x) = e^{3x} \ln(2x + 1)$.

A. Find the slope of the tangent line to the graph of $f(x)$ at any point.

   Answer: $3e^{3x} \ln(2x + 1) + \dfrac{2e^{3x}}{2x+1}$

B. Give an equation of the tangent line to the graph of $f(x)$ at $x = 0$.

   Answer: $y = 2x$

75. If $y = \ln(4x^2 + 1)$, find $\dfrac{dy}{dx}$.

   a) $\dfrac{1}{4x^2+1}$ b) $\ln 8x$ c) $\dfrac{8x}{4x^2+1}$ d) $\dfrac{1}{x}$ e) None of the above

   Answer: $\dfrac{8x}{4x^2+1}$

76. If $f(x) = (\ln x)^3$, find $f'(x)$.

   a) $3(\ln x)^2$ b) $\dfrac{3(\ln x)^2}{x}$ c) $\dfrac{3(\ln x)}{x}$ d) $\dfrac{3}{x}$ e) None of the above

   Answer: $\dfrac{3(\ln x)^2}{x}$

77. Find the minimum value of the function $f(x) = x \ln x$.

   a) $\dfrac{-1}{e}$ b) $\dfrac{1}{e}$ c) 0 d) $\dfrac{1}{e^2}$ e) $-\infty$

   Answer: $\dfrac{-1}{e}$

78. Find the minimum value of the function $f(x) = x - \ln x$.

   a) 1   b) 0   c) -1   d) $\frac{1}{e}$ e) $-\infty$

   Answer: 1

79. Find $f'(x)$ if $f(x) = x \ln(x^2 + 1)$

   Answer: $\frac{2x^2}{x^2+1} + \ln(x^2 + 1)$

80. If $y = \frac{\ln x}{3x}$, find $\frac{dy}{dx}$.

   Answer: $\frac{1-\ln x}{3x^2}$

81. If $y = \frac{\ln x^2}{3x}$, find $\frac{dy}{dx}$.

   Answer: $\frac{2-2\ln x}{3x^2}$

82. Let $f(x) = 4\left(2^{-x^2}\right)$.

A. What are the critical points of f?

   Answer: 0

B. What is the absolute maximum of f in the interval $-3 \le x \le 3$.

   Answer: 4

83. Find $\frac{dy}{dx}$ when $y = \ln(2x^2 + 3x - 5)$.

   Answer: $\frac{4x+3}{2x^2+3x-5}$

84. Find y' when $y = \ln\left(\frac{x-1}{x^2}\right)$.

Answer: $\dfrac{2-x}{x(x-1)}$

85. Find y' when $y = \ln e^x$.

Answer: 1

86. Find the derivative of $y = e^{\ln x}$.

Answer: 1

87. Find $\dfrac{dy}{dx}$ for $y = x\ln x - x$.

Answer: $\ln x$

88. At the end of two hours, there are 18,000 bacteria alive in a certain culture that initially contained 10,000 bacteria.

A. Find the exponential growth rate at any time t (in hours).

Answer: $10,000 e^{\frac{t}{2}\ln\frac{9}{5}}$ or $10,000\left(\frac{9}{5}\right)^{\frac{t}{2}}$

B. Find the number of bacteria present in the culture at the end of 3 hours. (Round to the nearest whole number)

Answer: 24,150 bacteria

89. The graphs of which of the following exhibit exponential growth?

a) $y = 10^x$ b) $y = e^x$ c) $y = \left(\frac{1}{2}\right)^{-x}$
d) All of them   e) None of them

Answer: All of them

107

90. The graphs of which of the following exhibit exponential decay?

   a) $y = e^{-x}$ b) $y = \left(\frac{1}{2}\right)^x$ c) $y = 3^{-x}$
   d) All of them   e) None of them

   Answer: All of them

91. A certain very active bacteria grows exponentially as given by the equation

   $A = A_0 e^{\frac{\ln 100}{10} t}$, where A_0 is the initial bacterial count, A is the final amount, and t is the time in hours. If we begin with 600 bacteria, how many will there be after one full day?

   Answer: $\approx$ 38 million

92. Use the laws of exponents to simplify the expression: $\dfrac{(b^{x-1})^y a^{x-1} a^{x+y+1}}{a^{2x} b^{xy}}$

   Answer: $\left(\frac{a}{b}\right)^y$

93. Solve the following equation without the use of logarithms. $3^{x^2-5} \cdot 3^x = 27\left(3^{x+1}\right)$

   Answer: $-3,\ 3$

94. For the exponential function $y = \left(\frac{1}{2}\right)^x$, state its domain, range, interval of continuity, interval of increasing or decreasing, and the points of intersection with the axes.

   Answer: Domain $(-\infty, \infty)$
               Range $(0, \infty)$
               Continuous on $(-\infty, \infty)$
               Decreasing on $(-\infty, \infty)$
               Passing through the point $(0, 1)$

95. For what real values of x is the logarithm of x to the base b defined?

   Answer: $(0, \infty)$

96. Use the laws of logarithms to simplify the expression: $e^{\ln\left(\ln e^{(x^2+1)}\right)}$.

Answer: $x^2 + 1$

97. Simplify the expression: $\dfrac{\log_e 4 \cdot \log_2 1}{\log_2 2 \cdot \log_e 2}$

Answer: 0

98. On what interval is the relation $e^{\ln x} = x$ valid? On what interval is the relation $\ln e^x = x$ valid?

Answer: $(0, \infty)$; $(-\infty, \infty)$

99. Solve the equation $20 - e^{0.5t} = 10$.

Answer: $t = 2\ln 10$

100. Solve the equation $6\ln x^2 - 10 = 0$

Answer: $e^{\frac{5}{6}}$

101. Determine the total accumulated amount after 10 years if $500 is invested at 10% per year compounded monthly. How many months will it take to double the amount?

Answer: $1353.52; 84 months

102. Find the monthly interest rate on your savings account if the effective rate is 4%.

Answer: $\approx 3.93\%$

103. If a savings account pays 6% interest compounded monthly, determine the amount of money needed to be placed in a savings account now to have at least $25,000 in five years.

    Answer: $18,534.31

104. Determine the amount of money accumulated if $1 is compounded continuously at 100% per year for one year.

    Answer: $2.72

105. Find the following derivatives:

    A. $\dfrac{d^5(e^x)}{dx^5}$

        Answer: e^x

    B. $\dfrac{d^5(e^{10x})}{dx^5}$

        Answer: $10^5 e^{10x}$

    C. $\dfrac{d^3(e^{2x}+e^{-2x})}{dx^3}$

        Answer: $8(e^{2x}-e^{-2x})$

106. Evaluate the expression $\dfrac{d^2}{dx^2}\{\ln[f(x)g(x)]^m\}$ where $f(x)$ and $g(x)$ are greater than zero.

    Answer: $m\left[\dfrac{f''f-(f')^2}{f^2}+\dfrac{g''g-(g')^2}{g^2}\right]$

107. Use logarithmic differentiation to find $f'(x)$ where $f(x)=e^x(x+1)^2(x+2)^4(x+3)^6$.

    Answer: $f(x)=e^x(x+1)^2(x+2)^4(x+3)^6\left(1+\dfrac{2}{x+1}+\dfrac{4}{x+2}+\dfrac{6}{x+3}\right).$

108. Use logarithmic differentiation to find $f'(x)$ where $f(x) = x^{(x^2+1)}$, $x > 0$.

Answer: $x^{x^2}\left(1 + x^2(2\ln x) + 1\right)$

109. Determine the approximate age of an archeological artifact if $\frac{1}{3}$ of the original amount of carbon-14 is present in the artifact. The decay constant for carbon-14 is 0.00012.

Answer: ≈ 9160 years

110. Find an expression for the remaining mass of a radioactive substance in terms of the decay time t (in days) and the original mass Q_0. The half-life is 140 days.

Answer: $Q(t) = Q_0 2^{\frac{-t}{140}}$

APPLIED CALCULUS

CHAPTER 6
INTEGRATION

1. Evaluate the following indefinite integral: $\int\left(\frac{1}{\sqrt[3]{3x}}+e^x+\frac{9}{x}+\frac{x^5}{9}\right)dx$.

   Answer: $\dfrac{\sqrt[3]{9x^2}}{2}+e^x+\ln|x|^9+\dfrac{x^6}{54}+C$

2. Find the function $f(x)$ such that the graph of f passes through the point $(-1,0)$ given that the slope of the tangent line to the graph at any point $(x,f(x))$ is $f'(x)=4x^3-6x^2+6x-3$.

   Answer: $x^4-2x^3+3x^2-3x-9$

3. Evaluate the following indefinite integral: $\int(\sqrt{x}+3)^2\left(6+\frac{6}{x}\right)dx$.

   Answer: $3x^2+24x^{\frac{3}{2}}+60x+72\sqrt{x}+54\ln|x|+C$

4. The daily marginal profit associated with the production and sales of a certain product is $P'(x)=-0.000024x^2+6$ (in dollars per production lot), where x represents the number of production lots produced and sold each day. Each production lot consists of 10 individual units.

   A. What is the total daily profit realizable from the production and sale of 5000 units per day if the daily fixed cost is $200 ($P(0)=-200$)?

   Answer: $1800

   B. What is the additional daily profit realizable if the production and sales are increased by 500 units per day?

   Answer: loss of $31

5. Evaluate: $\int \sqrt{x}(x+2)dx$.

a) $\frac{2}{15}x^{\frac{3}{2}}(3x+10)+C$

b) $\frac{1}{3}x^{\frac{5}{2}}(x+4)+C$

c) $\frac{3x+2}{2\sqrt{x}}+C$

d) $\frac{2(3x+10)}{15x\sqrt{x}}+C$

e) None of the above

Answer: $\frac{2}{15}x^{\frac{3}{2}}(3x+10)+C$

6. Evaluate: $\int\left(x^4-\frac{1}{x^3}\right)dx$.

a) x^5+x^4+C

b) $\frac{x^5}{5}-\frac{x^2}{2}+C$

c) $\frac{x^5}{5}-\frac{x^{-2}}{2}+C$

d) $\frac{1}{10x^2}\left(2x^7+5\right)+C$

e) None of the above

Answer: $\frac{1}{10x^2}\left(2x^7+5\right)+C$

7. If $f'(x)=2x-3x^2$ and $f(2)=-2$, find $f(x)$.

a) $2-6x$

b) x^2-x^3

c) x^2-x^3-2

d) x^2-x^3+2

e) None of the above

Answer: x^2-x^3+2

8. If $f'(x)=\frac{1}{\sqrt{x}}+2$ and $f(1)=4$, find $f(x)$.

a) $2\sqrt{x}+2x+4$

b) $-\frac{2}{x}+2x$

c) $2\sqrt{x}+2x$

d) $-\frac{1}{2\sqrt{x^3}}+4$

e) None of the above

Answer: $2\sqrt{x}+2x$

9. Evaluate: $\int 3x^5 dx$.

Answer: $\frac{x^6}{2}+C$

10. Evaluate: $\int \frac{2}{\sqrt{x}}\,dx$.

   <u>Answer:</u> $4\sqrt{x} + C$

11. Evaluate: $\int \left(e^{-x} - \frac{1}{x}\right)dx$.

   <u>Answer:</u> $-e^{-x} - \ln x + C$

12. The marginal revenue for a product is given by $R'(x) = 20 + 3x$, where x is measured in hundreds and the revenue is measured in thousands of dollars. Find the revenue Function.

   <u>Answer:</u> $R(x) = 20x + \frac{3}{2}x^2$

13. **Graphics Calculator Question**

A. Using either a graphics calculator or graphing software, graph each of the following antiderivatives of $f(x) = 2x - 3x^2$.

   i) $y = x^2 - x^3$ ii) $y = 1 + x^2 - x^3$ iii) $y = -1 + x^2 - x^3$

   <u>Answer:</u>

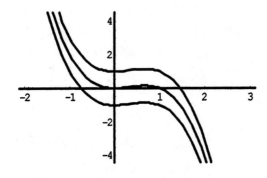

B.   Calculate and draw the tangent line to each these antiderivatives at $x = 1$.

Answer:

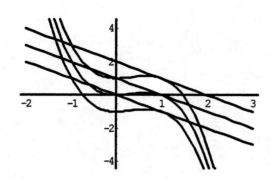

14.   Evaluate: $\int\left(x - \frac{1}{e^x}\right)dx$.

a $\frac{x^2}{2} - \ln e^x + C$ b) $\frac{x^2}{2} + e^{-x} + C$ c) $\frac{x^2}{2} - \frac{1}{e^{2x}} + C$

d) $\frac{x^2}{2} - \frac{1}{e^x} + C$ e) None of the above

Answer: $\frac{x^2}{2} + e^{-x} + C$

15.   Find: $\int x^5 dx$

Answer: $\frac{x^6}{6} + C$

16.   Find: $\int dx$

Answer: $x + C$

17.   Find: $\int t^{-5} dt$

Answer: $\frac{t^{-4}}{-4} + C$

18.   Find: $\int e^y dy$.

Answer: $e^y + C$

19. Find: $\int x^{\frac{5}{3}} dx$.

Answer: $\dfrac{3x^{\frac{8}{3}}}{8} + C$

20. Find: $\int (6x^3 + 4x - 6) dx$.

Answer: $\frac{3}{2}x^4 + 2x^2 - 6x + C$

21. Find: $\int (x + x^{-1}) dx$.

Answer: $\frac{1}{2}x^2 + \ln|x| + C$

22. Find: $\int \left(x^{\frac{1}{3}} + x^{\frac{-1}{3}} \right)^2 dx$

Answer: $\frac{3}{5}x^{\frac{5}{3}} + 2x + 3x^{\frac{1}{3}} + C$

23. Find the antiderivative, F of $f(x) = 5x^2 - 3x + 7$, given that $F(0) = 11$.

Answer: $\frac{5}{3}x^3 - \frac{3}{2}x^2 + 7x + 11$

24. Find the antiderivative, F of $f(x) = 5x^2 - 3x + 7$, given that $F(2) = 1$.

Answer: $\frac{5}{3}x^3 - \frac{3}{2}x^2 + 7x - \frac{61}{3}$

25. Find the antiderivative, F of $f(x) = 4x^3 + 6x^2 - 2x + 5$, given that $F(0) = 5$.

Answer: $x^4 + 2x^3 - x^2 + 5x + 5$

26. Find the antiderivative, F of $f(x) = 4x^3 + 6x^2 - 2x + 5$, given that $F(2) = -18$.

Answer: $x^4 + 2x^3 - x^2 + 5x - 56$

27. Find the antiderivative, F of $f(x) = x^{\frac{2}{3}} - 2x^{\frac{1}{3}} + 1$, given that $F(0) = 4$.

Answer: $\frac{3}{5}x^{\frac{5}{3}} - \frac{3}{2}x^{\frac{4}{3}} + x + 4$

28. Find the antiderivative, F of $f(x) = x^{\frac{2}{3}} - 2x^{\frac{1}{3}} + 1$, given that $F(8) = 4$.

Answer: $\frac{3}{5}x^{\frac{5}{3}} - \frac{3}{2}x^{\frac{4}{3}} + x + \frac{4}{5}$

29. Find the antiderivative, F of $f(x) = \frac{x^2 + 5x + 6}{x + 2}$, given that $F(0) = 4$.

Answer: $x^2 + 3x$

30. If the divorce rate in a community is given by $10t - 6t^2$, where t is the number of years after 1980, give the number of divorces (to the nearest hundred) in 1988 if it is known that the number of divorces in 1985 was 2500.

Answer: 1900 divorces

31. A young tree grows at the rate of $\frac{dh}{dt} = \sqrt[3]{t}$, where h is the height (in feet) of the tree at the end of year t after planting. If the tree is one foot tall when it was planted, what is the height after 5 years?

Answer: $7\frac{1}{2}$ ft

32. Evaluate: $\int \frac{x^2 + 3x - 1}{x^3} dx$.

Answer: $\ln|x| - 3x^{-1} + \frac{1}{2}x^{-2} + C$

33. Evaluate: $\int \frac{2x^3 + x^2 + x + 14}{x + 2} dx$.

Answer: $\frac{2}{3}x^3 - \frac{3}{2}x^2 + 7x + C$

34. Suppose the marginal cost of producing x copies of a book is given by $C'(x) = 100x^{\frac{-1}{2}}$, and it is known that $C(0) = 85,000$. Find the cost (to the nearest dollar) of producing 25,000 books.

Answer: $116,623

35. A manufacturing company has a marginal cost of $C'(x) = 6 - 0.0004x$. If the cost of producing 100 units is $9098, find the total cost equation and the cost of producing 12,000 units.

Answer: $C = 6x - 0.0002x^2 + 85000$; $C(12,000) = \$51,800$

36. Use an appropriate substitution to evaluate the following indefinite integral:

$$\int \frac{x}{3x+4}\,dx.$$

Answer: $\frac{1}{9}(3x - 4\ln|3x+4|) + C$

37. Use an appropriate substitution to evaluate the following indefinite integral:

$$\int \frac{4x^7}{\sqrt{4-x^4}}\,dx.$$

Answer: $\frac{-2}{3}\sqrt{4-x^4}\left(x^4+8\right) + C$

38. Evaluate: $\int \frac{3x}{\sqrt{1-x^2}}\,dx.$

a) $\frac{-3}{2}\sqrt{1-x^2} + C$ b) $\frac{-3}{4}\sqrt{1-x^2} + C$ c) $-3\sqrt{1-x^2} + C$

d) $3\sqrt{1-x^2} + C$ e) None of the above

Answer: $-3\sqrt{1-x^2} + C$

39. Evaluate: $\int \frac{\ln x}{x} dx$.

   a) $\frac{-2}{x^3} + C$

   b) $\frac{-1}{x^2} + C$

   c) $\frac{(\ln x)^2}{2} + C$

   d) $\ln(x^2) + C$

   e) None of the above

   Answer: $\frac{(\ln x)^2}{2} + C$

40. Evaluate: $\int \frac{6x}{\sqrt[3]{1-x^2}} dx$.

   a) $\frac{-9}{2}(1-x^2)^{\frac{2}{3}} + C$

   b) $-9(1-x^2)^{\frac{2}{3}} + C$

   c) $18(1-x^2)^{\frac{1}{3}} + C$

   d) $18(1-x^2)^{\frac{2}{3}} + C$

   e) None of the above

   Answer: $\frac{-9}{2}(1-x^2)^{\frac{2}{3}} + C$

41. Evaluate: $\int e^{-4x} dx$.

   a) $-4e^{-4x} + C$

   b) $e^{-4x} + C$

   c) $-e^{-4x} + C$

   d) $-\frac{1}{4}e^{-4x} + C$

   e) None of the above

   Answer: $-\frac{1}{4}e^{-4x} + C$

42. Evaluate: $\int x^2 e^{3x^3} dx$.

   Answer: $\frac{1}{9}e^{3x^3} + C$

43. Evaluate: $\int \frac{y^2}{\sqrt{y^3-1}} dy$.

   Answer: $\frac{2}{3}\sqrt{y^3-1} + C$

119

44. Evaluate: $\int \frac{\ln y}{2y} dy$

Answer: $\frac{(\ln y)^2}{4} + C$

45. Evaluate: $\int t^2(1-t^3)^5 dt$

Answer: $-\frac{(1-t^3)^6}{18} + C$

46. Evaluate: $\int t\sqrt{t-2}\, dt$

Answer: $\frac{2(t-2)^{\frac{5}{2}}}{5} + \frac{4(t-2)^{\frac{3}{2}}}{3} + C$

47. Find: $\int e^{-1} dt$.

Answer: $\frac{t}{e} + C$

48. Find: $\int \frac{dx}{x+5}$.

Answer: $\ln|x+5| + C$

49. Evaluate: $\int (12-6x^2)^7 x\, dx$

Answer: $-\frac{(12-6x^2)^8}{96} + C$

50. Evaluate: $\int (e^{5x-2} + e^{-1}) dx$

Answer: $\frac{1}{5}e^{5x-2} + xe^{-1} + C$

51. Find: $\int \frac{(x^2+2)dx}{x^3+6x}$.

Answer: $\frac{1}{3}\ln|x^3+6x| + C$

120

52. Find: $\int x^2 \sqrt{5-x}\, dx$

Answer: $-\frac{50}{3}(5-x)^{\frac{3}{2}} + 4(5-x)^{\frac{5}{2}} - \frac{2}{7}(5-x)^{\frac{7}{2}} + C$

53. Evaluate: $\int e^{x^2 + \ln 2x + 3}\, dt$

Answer: $e^{x^2 + 3} + C$

54. The marginal profit for a business is modeled by the formula $\frac{dP}{dt} = \frac{500t}{\sqrt{t^2+1}}$. Find a function for the daily profit if the profit when $t = 0$ is \$100.

Answer: $P(t) = 500\sqrt{t^2 + 1} - 400$

55. Radioactive substances decay at a rate proportional to the amount present at any given time: $\frac{dA}{dt} = kA$. Carbon -14, used fro archaeological dating has a half-life of about 5750 years. If A_0 is the amount present at time $t = 0$, find the constant of proportionality, k, and then find what percent of carbon -14 would remain after 2000 years.

Answer: $k = \ln\frac{1}{5750} \approx -0.000120547$, so $\frac{A_0}{A} = e^{-0.000120547(2000)} \approx 78.6\%$

56. Evaluate: $\int \frac{\ln^3 x}{x}\, dx$.

Answer: $\frac{1}{4}\ln^4 x + C$

57. Evaluate: $\int x(3 - 4x)^3\, dx$.

Answer: $-\frac{3}{64}(3 - 4x)^4 + \frac{1}{80}(3 - 4x)^5 + C$

58. Evaluate: $\int xe^{4x^2 + 3}\, dx$.

Answer: $\frac{1}{8}e^{4x^2 + 3} + C$

59. Find the area of the region under $y = x^2 - 3x$ from $x = 4$ to $x = 8$.

Answer: $\frac{232}{3}$ square units

60. Find Riemann sum approximations of the area of the region under $f(x) = 3 + \frac{1}{x+1}$ over the interval [0, 5] by partitioning the interval into two subintervals of equal length, where the points p_i, $1 \le i \le n$, of the respective subintervals are taken to be:

A. The left endpoints

Answer: $\frac{255}{14}$ square units

B. The right endpoints

Answer: $\frac{1355}{14}$ square units

C. The midpoints

Answer: $\frac{2845}{171}$ square units

61. If the marginal cost (in dollars) for producing x units of a particular product is given by $C'(x) = 0.2x + 20$, and the fixed cost is $1500, find $C(x)$.

Answer: $0.1x^2 + 20x + 1500$

62. If the marginal cost (in dollars) for producing x units of a particular product is given by $C'(x) = 0.4x + 100$, and the fixed cost is $3500, find $C(x)$.

Answer: $0.2x^2 + 100x + 3500$

63.   Approximate the area under $y = \ln x$ from $x = 1$ to $x = 6$ using 8 "left" rectangles.

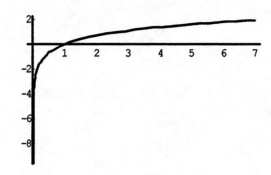

Answer: 5.163889

64.   Find the area of the region under $y = e^{-5x} + 1$ from $x = 0$ to $x = 2$.

Answer: $2 + \frac{1}{5}\left(1 - e^{-10}\right) \approx 2.2$

65.   Find the average value of $f(x) = x^2 - 4x - 5$ over the interval $[-1, 1]$.

Answer: $\frac{-14}{3}$

66.   Find the area of the region bounded by $f(x) = x^3 + 1$, $x = 0$, $x = 2$ and the x–axis.

a) 18 square units   b) 6 square units   c) 5 square units
d) 12 square units   e) None of the above

Answer: 6 square units

67.   Find the area of the region bounded by $f(x) = \frac{1}{x^2}$, $x = 1$, $x = 2$ and the x–axis.

a) 4 square units   b) $\frac{7}{4}$ square units   c) $2\sqrt{2}$ square units
d) $\frac{1}{2}$ square units   e) None of the above

Answer: $\frac{1}{2}$ square units

68. Find the area of the region bounded by $y = e^{3x}$, $x = 0$, $x = 1$ and the x-axis. Round the answer to two decimal places.

Answer: 6.36

69. Find the area of the region bounded by $y = \frac{1}{x}$, $x = 1$, $x = 2$ and the x-axis. Round the answer to two decimal places.

Answer: 0.69

70. Find: $\displaystyle\int_0^4 \sqrt{x}(1 - \sqrt{x})dx$.

Answer: $\dfrac{-8}{3}$

71. Find the area bounded by $f(x) = 3x + 5$, the x-axis, and the lines $x = 1$ to $x = 4$.

Answer: $\dfrac{75}{2}$

72. Find the area bounded by $y = 3x^2 - x - 10$, the x-axis, and the lines $x = 1$ and $x = 4$.

Answer: $\dfrac{69}{2}$

73. Find the area bounded by $y = e^{3x-1}$, the x-axis, and the lines $x = 0$ and $x = 3$.

Answer: $\dfrac{1}{3}\left(e^2 - e^{-1}\right) \approx 2.3403$

74. Find the area bounded by $f(x) = (x + 1)^{-1}$, the x-axis and the lines $x = 0$ and $x = 3$.

Answer: $\ln 4 \approx 1.38629$

75. Find the area bounded by the parabola $y = 6 - x - x^2$ and the x-axis.

Answer: $20\dfrac{5}{6}$

124

76. What is the average value of $f(x) = 6x^2 - 4x + 5$ on $[-3, 3]$?

Answer: 23

77. What is the average value of $f(x) = \frac{\ln x}{x}$ on $[1, 5]$ correct to two decimal places?

Answer: 0.40

78. What is the average value of $f(x) = \frac{e^x}{1+e^x}$ on $[0, 10]$ correct to two decimal places?

Answer: 0.93

79. What is the average value of $f(x) = (x+4)(x-3)^3$ on $[-4, 3]$?

Answer: $\frac{-2401}{20}$

80. What is the average value of $f(x) = x^3 + e^{\frac{x}{2}} + 6$ on $[1, 4]$ correct to two decimal places?

Answer: 31.0769

81. Suppose the rate of change in profit (in thousands of dollars) is modeled by the equation: $P(m) = (10 - m)^2$, where m is the month of the year. Find the average change in profit (to the nearest dollar) over a year ($m = 0$ to $m = 12$).

Answer: $\approx \$28,000$

82. Evaluate the following definite integral: $\int_{0}^{2} 4x(x+4)(x-4)dx$.

Answer: -112

83. Given the definite integral $\displaystyle\int_0^1 \frac{x}{\sqrt{16-7x^2}}\,dx$, use an appropriate substitution and the Properties of definite integrals to:

A. Find an equivalent definite integral to be integrated and evaluated with respect to u.

Answer: $\displaystyle\frac{1}{14}\int_9^{16}\frac{du}{\sqrt{u}}$

B. Evaluate the integral.

Answer: $\displaystyle\frac{1}{7}$

84. Evaluate: $\displaystyle\int_0^1 (1-2x)^3\,dx$.

a) 0   b) $-\frac{1}{8}$ c) $-\frac{81}{8}$ d) $\frac{1}{4}$ e) None of the above

Answer: 0

85. Evaluate: $\displaystyle\int_1^2 x\sqrt{5-x^2}\,dx$.

a) $\frac{7}{2}$ b) $-\frac{7}{3}$ c) $\frac{21}{4}$ d) $\frac{7}{3}$ e) None of the above

Answer: $\frac{7}{3}$

86. Find the average value for $f(x)=9-x^2$ between $x=0$ and $x=3$.

a) 18   b) 6   c) 9   d) $\frac{27}{4}$ e) None of the above

Answer: 6

87. Find the average value for $f(x) = 4 - x^2$ between $x = -1$ and $x = 1$.

   a) $\dfrac{22}{3}$ b) 4   c) $\dfrac{13}{6}$ d) $\dfrac{5}{3}$ e) None of the above

   Answer: $\dfrac{13}{6}$

88. Evaluate: $\displaystyle\int_{1}^{3} (x^2 - x + 1)\,dx$.

   Answer: $\dfrac{20}{3}$

89. Evaluate: $\displaystyle\int_{0}^{1} \dfrac{1}{5-x}\,dx$.

   Answer: $\ln 5 - \ln 4$

90. Evaluate: $\displaystyle\int_{\sqrt{3}}^{\sqrt{8}} \dfrac{dx}{x\sqrt{x^2+1}}$.

   Answer: $\ln\dfrac{\sqrt{2}}{2} - \dfrac{\sqrt{3}}{3} \approx 0,202732554$

91. Evaluate: $\displaystyle\int_{0}^{2} \sqrt{4x+1}\,dx$.

   Answer: $\dfrac{13}{3}$

92. Sketch the graph and find the area of the region bounded by $f(x) = 2 - \frac{1}{3}x$,

$g(x) = 5 - \frac{5}{6}x$ and the vertical line $x = 0$.

<u>Answer:</u> Area = 9 square units

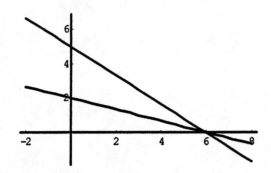

93. Sketch the graph and find the area of the region completely enclosed by
$f(x) = -x^2 + 4x$ and $g(x) = 2x - 8$.

<u>Answer:</u> Area = 36 square units

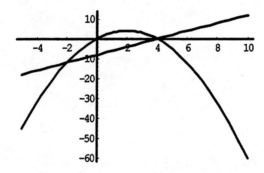

94. Find the area between the two curves $y = x$ and $y = x^2 - 2x$.

a) $\frac{7}{6}$ square units

b) $\frac{10}{3}$ square units

c) $\frac{9}{2}$ square units

d) $\frac{1}{6}$ square units

e) None of the above

<u>Answer:</u> $\frac{9}{2}$ square units

95. Find the area between the two curves $y = -x^2$ and $y = x^2 - 2x$.

a) $\frac{2}{3}$ square unit   b) $\frac{1}{3}$ square unit   c) $\frac{5}{3}$ square units

d) 1 square unit   e) None of the above

Answer: $\frac{1}{3}$ square unit

96. Find the area between the curves $f(x) = x$ and $g(x) = x^3$ from $x = -1$ to $x = 1$.

Answer: $\frac{1}{2}$

97. Find the area between the curves $f(x) = e^x$ and $g(x) = e^{-x}$ from $x = 0$ to $x = 1$.

Answer: 1.08616

98. Find the area between the curves $f(x) = 3x$ and $g(x) = x^3 - 6x$.

Answer: $\frac{81}{4}$

99. Find the area between the curves $f(x) = -x$ and $g(x) = 2 - x^2$.

Answer: $\frac{9}{2}$

100. If the growth rate of a city is given by the formula $P'(x) = .25e^{.02t}$, where t is measured in years after 1985 and $P(t)$ is the population in thousands. If the population in 1987 was 35,000, predict the population (to the nearest hundred) at the turn of the century.

Answer: 38,900

101. Mr. And Mrs. Abbot are selling some property they own and have agreed to carry their own paper, subject to the following terms: The buyer is to make a down payment of $14,000 and equal monthly payments of $650 per month for 15 years. Find the present value of the purchase price of the property to the nearest dollar if the prevailing interest rate is 12 percent per annum compounded continuously.

Answer: $68,256

102. Find the consumer surplus given that the demand equation is $p = 500 - 10x$ and the supply equation is $p = 0.5x^2 + 100$ for a certain product, and the price is set at the equilibrium price.

Answer: $2000

103. Find the producer surplus given that the demand equation is $p = 500 - 10x$ and the supply equation is $p = 0.5x^2 + 100$ for a certain product, and the price is set at the equilibrium price.

Answer: $2667

104. Find the cost function for $C'(x) = 12x^2 + 5$ if the fixed costs are $8000.

Answer: $C(x) = 4x^3 + 5x + 8000$

105. Find the cost function for $C'(x) = 500 + 15.5x$ if the fixed costs are $25,000.

Answer: $C'(x) = 25,000 + 500x + \frac{31}{4}x^2$

106. Find the cost function for $C'(x) = .002x^3$ if the fixed costs are $12,500.

Answer: $C'(x) = 0.0005x^4 + 12,500$

107. Find the cost function for $C'(x) = 500 + 15.5x$ if the fixed costs are $25,000.

Answer: $C'(x) = 25,000 + 500x + \frac{31}{4}x^2$

108. Find the cost function for $C'(x) = 2000 + 5x + x^{\frac{2}{3}}$ if the fixed costs are $5,000.

Answer: $C'(x) = 5,000 + \frac{5}{2}x^2 + \frac{3}{5}x^{\frac{5}{3}}$

109. If the rate of flow for an investment is $f(t) = 20,000$, find the total income produced in 7 years.

Answer: $140,000

110. If the rate of flow for an investment is $f(t) = 20,000e^{.09t}$, find the total income produced in 7 years.

Answer: $195,024.57

111. If the rate of flow for an investment is $f(t) = 20,000e^{.09t}$, find the total income produced from year 3 to year 5.

Answer: $57,410.61

112. If the rate of flow for an investment is $f(t) = 100e^{.08t}$, find the total income produced in 5 years.

Answer: $614.78

113. If the rate of flow for an investment is $f(t) = 100e^{.08t}$, find the total income produced from year 5 to year 10.
years.

Answer: $917.15

114. What is the total money flow for $5000 at 5% for 5 years?

Answer: $24,402.54

115. What is the total money flow for $10,000 at 15% for 8 years?

Answer: $154,674.46

116. What is the total money flow for $120,000 at 8% for 10 years?

   Answer: $1,838,311.39

117. What is the total money flow for $50 at 10% for 30 years?

   Answer: $9542.77

118. What is the total money flow for $20,000 at 9% for 7 years?

   Answer: $195,024.57

119. The price, in dollars, for a product is $D(x) = 376 - 15x - x^2$. The supply curve, in dollars, is given by $S(x) = x^2 + 9x - 200$. Find the consumer's surplus if the price is set at the equilibrium price.

   Answer: $2232

120. The price, in dollars, for a product is $D(x) = 376 - 15x - x^2$. The supply curve, in dollars, is given by $S(x) = x^2 + 9x - 200$. Find the producer's surplus if the price is set at the equilibrium price.

   Answer: $1800

121. The price, in dollars, for a product is $D(x) = 950 - 25x - x^2$. The supply curve, in dollars, is given by $S(x) = x^2 - 15x - 50$. Find the consumer's surplus if the price is set at the equilibrium price.

   Answer: $10,333

122. The price, in dollars, for a product is $D(x) = 950 - 25x - x^2$. The supply curve, in dollars, is given by $S(x) = x^2 - 15x - 50$. Find the producer's surplus if the price is set at the equilibrium price.

   Answer: $2333

123. The price, in dollars, for a product is $D(x) = \dfrac{192+240x}{(x-4)^2}$. The supply curve, in dollars, is given by $S(x) = x + 12$. Write the necessary integral to find the consumer's surplus if the price is set at the equilibrium price.

Answer: $\displaystyle\int_{0}^{16}\left(\dfrac{192+240x}{(x-4)^2} - 28\right)dx$

124. A leasing company wants to decide on the monthly lease fee for a piece of equipment. The company expects to lease the piece of equipment for 1 year (12 months), and it expects the rate of maintenance, in dollars, to be modeled by the formula $M(t) = 100 - 3t + t^2$, where t is the number of months the equipment is used. Find the total maintenance charge for the one year period.

Answer: $1560

125. Evaluate $\displaystyle\int 3e^x dx$.

Answer: $3e^x + C$

126. Evaluate $\displaystyle\int \dfrac{u^4+u^2+1}{3u}du$.

Answer: $\dfrac{1}{3}\left(\dfrac{u^4}{4} + \dfrac{u^2}{2} + \ln|u|\right) + C$

127. Evaluate the indefinite integral $\displaystyle\int x^n dx$, for all n and $x > 0$.

Answer: $\dfrac{1}{n+1}x^{n+1} + C,\ n \neq -1;\quad \ln x + C,\ n = -1$

128. Evaluate the indefinite integral $\displaystyle\int\left(1 - \tfrac{1}{x}\right)^2 x^2 dx$.

Answer: $\tfrac{1}{3}x^3 - x^2 + x + C$

129. Determine the function $f(x)$ if $f'(x) = 2x^2 + 3x + 1$ and $f(0) = 0$.

Answer: $f(x) = \tfrac{2}{3}x^3 + \tfrac{3}{2}x^2 + x$

133

130. Which of the following is an antiderivative of $f(x) = xe^{-x} + 1$?

a) $F(x) = xe^{-x} + x + 1$
b) $F(x) = \frac{-x-1}{e^x} + x + 1$
c) $F(x) = xe^{-x} + e^{-x} + x + C$, where C is a constant
d) $F(x) = -xe^{-x} - e^{-x} + x + 2$
e) None of the above

<u>Answer:</u> $F(x) = -xe^{-x} - e^{-x} + x + 2$

131. Integrate the indefinite integral $\int 3xe^{x^2 - 1} dx$.

<u>Answer:</u> $\frac{3}{2}e^{x^2 - 1} + C$

132. Integrate the indefinite integral $\int \frac{3x}{x-2} dx$.

<u>Answer:</u> $6\ln|x - 2| + 3x + C$

133. State the Fundamental Theorem of Calculus.

<u>Answer:</u> Let f be continuous on $[a, b]$, then $\int_a^b f(x)dx = F(b) - F(a)$
where F is an antiderivative of f, that is $F'(x) = f(x)$.

134. Find the area under the curve $y = x\sqrt{4 - x^2}$ from $x = 0$ to $x = 2$.

<u>Answer:</u> $\frac{8}{3}$ square units

135. Evaluate $\int_{-1}^{1} (x^3 - 9x)dx$.

<u>Answer:</u> 0

136. Find the average value of $f(x) = x^{-1}$ over the interval $[1, 2]$.

Answer: $\ln 2$

137. If $\int_{-1}^{2} f(x)dx = 3$ evaluate $\int_{2}^{-1} f(x)dx$.

Answer: -3

138. Determine the definite integral in terms of u, complete with correct limits, if

$u = x^3 + 2$ and $\int_{0}^{1} 6x^2(x^3 + 2)^{\frac{1}{2}} dx$ (do not evaluate).

Answer: $2\int_{2}^{3} u^{\frac{1}{2}} du$

139. For polynomial functions $f(x)$ and $g(x)$ such that $f(x) \geq g(x)$. Find the area of the region bounded above by $y = f(x)$ and below by $y = g(x)$ on the interval $[c, d]$.

Answer: Area $= \int_{c}^{d} [f(x) - g(x)]dx$

140. Find the area enclosed by the curves $f(x) = x^2 + 2$ and $g(x) - x^2 + 4$.

Answer: $\frac{8}{3}$ square units

141. Derive a formula for the volume of a sphere as a solid of revolution if the equation of a semicircle is $y = \sqrt{R^2 - x^2}$ where R is the radius.

Answer: $\frac{4}{3}\pi R^3$

142. Find the volume of the solid of revolution obtained by revolving the region bounded by the curves $y = R$ and $y = r$ from $x = a$ to $x = b$.

Answer: $\pi(b - a)(R - r)^2$

135

APPLIED CALCULUS

CHAPTER 7
ADDITIONAL TOPICS IN INTEGRATION

1. Use integration by parts to evaluate the following indefinite integral: $\int (8x - 7)e^x dx$.

    Answer: $(8x - 7)e^x - 8e^x + C$

2. Use integration by parts to evaluate the following indefinite integral: $\int x^{-4}(\ln 3x)^2 dx$.

    Answer: $-\frac{1}{27}x^{-3}\left[9(\ln 3x)^2 + 6\ln 3x + 2\right] + C$

3. Evaluate the following indefinite integral: $\int 4x^3 e^{-x^2} dx$. (Hint: First substitute $u = -x^2$, then integrate by parts.)

    Answer: $-2e^{-x^2}(x^2 + 1) + C$

4. Evaluate: $\int xe^{-x}dx$.

    a) $-xe^{-x} + C$ b) $\frac{-x^2 e^{-x}}{2} + C$ c) $-xe^{-x} - e^{-x} + C$

    d) $\frac{-x^2 e^{-x}}{2} - e^{-x} + C$ e) None of the above

    Answer: $-xe^{-x} - e^{-x} + C$

5. Evaluate: $\int \ln \sqrt{x}\, dx$.

    a) $\frac{x}{2}\ln x - \frac{x}{2} + C$ b) $\frac{x}{2} + C$ c) $x\ln \sqrt{x} - \frac{2}{3}\sqrt{x^3} + C$

    d) $x\ln \sqrt{x} - \frac{1}{\sqrt{x}} + C$ e) None of the above

    Answer: $\frac{x}{2}\ln x - \frac{x}{2} + C$

6. Evaluate: $\int\limits_{1}^{3} \ln x\, dx$.

a) $-\dfrac{2}{3}$ b) $\dfrac{2}{3}$ c) $3(\ln 3 - 1)$

d) $3\ln 3 - 2$ e) None of the above

Answer: $3\ln 3 - 2$

7. Evaluate: $\int\limits_{1}^{4} \ln x\, dx$.

a) $-\dfrac{3}{4}$ b) $\dfrac{3}{4}$ c) $4(\ln 4 - 1)$

d) $4\ln 4 - 3$ e) None of the above

Answer: $4\ln 4 - 3$

8. Evaluate: $\int x^2 \ln 2x\, dx$.

Answer: $\dfrac{x^3}{9}(3\ln 2x - 1) + C$

9. Use a table of integrals to evaluate the following indefinite integral: $\int \left(64x^2 - 1\right)^{\frac{-3}{2}} dx$.

Answer: $-\dfrac{x}{\sqrt{64x^2-1}} + C$

10. Use a table of integrals to evaluate: $\int x^3 \ln x\, dx$.

Answer: $\dfrac{x^4}{16}(4\ln x - 1) + C$

11. Use a table of integrals to evaluate: $\int \dfrac{1}{1+e^{2x}}\, dx$.

Answer: $x - \ln\sqrt{1 + e^{2x}} + C$

12. Use a table of integrals to evaluate: $\int \frac{1}{3+e^{2x}} dx$.

Answer: $\frac{x}{3} - \frac{1}{6} \ln\left(3 + e^{2x}\right) + C$

13. Find $\int \frac{dx}{\sqrt{x^2-2}}$ using an integration table.

Answer: $\ln\left|x + \sqrt{x^2 - 2}\right| + C$

14. Find $\int xe^{5x} dx$ using an integration table.

Answer: $\frac{e^{5x}}{25}(5x - 1) + C$

15. Find $\int \frac{dx}{1-3e^{6x}}$ using an integration table.

Answer: $x - \frac{1}{6} \ln\left|1 - 3e^{6x}\right| + C$

16. Evaluate: $\int \frac{dx}{5-3e^{2x}}$.

Answer: $\frac{x}{5} - \frac{1}{10} \ln\left|5 - 3e^{2x}\right| + C$

17. Evaluate: $\int (3+x)e^x dx$.

Answer: $2e^x + xe^x + C$

18. In using the Trapezoid Rule to approximate $\int_1^5 x^4 dx$ with $n = 4$, $x_0 = 1$, $x_4 = 5$, find the value for x_2.

a) 2   b) 2.2   c) 3   d) 4   e) None of the above

Answer: 3

138

19. In using the Trapezoid Rule to approximate $\int_{2}^{5} x^4\,dx$ with $n=4$, $x_0=2$, $x_4=5$, find the value for x_3.

    a) 3.5   b) 4.67   c) 3   d) 2.75   e) None of the above

    Answer: 3

20. Approximate (round to four decimal places) the integral below using the Trapezoid Rule with $n=4$.

$$\int_{0}^{1} e^{x^2}\,dx$$

    Answer: 1.4907

21. Approximate (round to four decimal places) the integral below using the Trapezoid Rule with $n=6$.

$$\int_{0}^{3} e^{-x^2}\,dx$$

    Answer: 0.8862

22. Approximate (round to four decimal places) the integral below using Simpson's Rule with $n=6$.

$$\int_{0}^{3} e^{-x^2}\,dx$$

    Answer: 0.8862

23. Approximate (round to four decimal places) the integral below using Simpson's Rule with $n=4$.

$$\int_{0}^{1} e^{x^2}\,dx$$

    Answer: 1.4637

139

24. Estimate $\int_0^{10} f(x)dx$ by finding $\sum_0^5 f(x)\Delta x$ for:

x	=	1	3	5	7	9
$f(x)$	=	36	52	63	85	93

Answer: 658

25. Estimate $\int_0^3 f(x)dx$ by finding $\sum_0^6 f(x)\Delta x$ for:

x	=	0.5	1.0	1.5	2.0	2.5	3.0
$f(x)$	=	1.7	2.1	2.5	2.1	1.6	1.3

Answer: 5.65

26. A marine biologist wishes to know the area of a small lake. She finds the length to be 210 feet. The widths at 30 ft intervals are recorded as:

x	=	30	60	90	120	150	180	210
$f(x)$	=	54	83	95	110	102	49	38

Use the data to approximate the area of the lake.

Answer: 16,000 sq. Ft.

27. A farmer has an irregularly shaped field of buckwheat, and would like to know the acreage. He finds the length to be 505 ft. And the width at 100 ft intervals to be:

x	=	100	200	300	400	500
$f(x)$ = width	=	210	190	170	220	230

Use the data to estimate the acreage (1 acre = 43,560 sq. ft.)

Answer: 2.6 acres

28. Estimate the area of an ellipse centered at the origin with major axis of 6 along the x – axis, given the following first quadrant points on the ellipse: $(0.5, 1.98)$, $(1.0, 1.89)$, $(1.5, 1.73)$, $(2.0, 1.49)$, $(2.5, 1.11)$, $(3.0, 0)$.

Answer: 16.4

29. Approximate $\displaystyle\int_0^1 x^3 \, dx$ using a trapezoidal approximation where $n = 2$.

Answer: 0.3125

30. Approximate $\displaystyle\int_0^1 x^3 \, dx$ using a trapezoidal approximation where $n = 4$.

Answer: 0.265625

31. Approximate $\displaystyle\int_{-1}^1 \sqrt{x^3 + 1} \, dx$ using a trapezoidal approximation where $n = 4$.

Answer: 1.851590650

32. Approximate $\displaystyle\int_{-1}^1 \sqrt{x^3 + 1} \, dx$ using a trapezoidal approximation where $n = 8$.

Answer: 1.913972394

33. Approximate $\displaystyle\int_1^2 \frac{1}{x^2} \, dx$ using a trapezoidal approximation where $n = 2$.

Answer: 0.534722222

34. Approximate $\int_0^1 x^3 \, dx$ using Simpson's Rule where $n = 4$.

Answer: 0.25

35. Approximate $\int_{-1}^1 \sqrt{x^3 + 1} \, dx$ using Simpson's Rule where $n = 4$.

Answer: 1.899751940

36. Approximate $\int_0^2 x e^x \, dx$ using Simpson's Rule where $n = 4$.

Answer: 8.400375470

37. Approximate $\int_0^2 x e^x \, dx$ using Simpson's Rule where $n = 8$.

Answer: 8.389785277

38. Approximate $\int_1^2 \frac{1}{x^2} \, dx$ using Simpson's Rule where $n = 4$.

Answer: 0.500417611

39. Evaluate the following improper integral if it is convergent: $\int_2^\infty 4(2x + 1)^{-2} \, dx$.

Answer: $\frac{2}{5}$

40. Find the area of the region under $f(x) = 7e^{-4x}$ over the interval $[0, \infty)$.

Answer: $\frac{7}{4}$ square units

41. Which of the following improper integrals converge?

a) $\int_1^\infty \frac{1}{x^3}dx$ b) $\int_1^\infty \frac{1}{\sqrt[3]{x}}dx$ c) $\int_1^\infty \frac{dx}{\sqrt{x+4}}$ d) $\int_1^\infty \frac{1}{x}dx$ e) None of the above

Answer: $\int_1^\infty \frac{1}{x^3}dx$

42. Which of the following improper integrals converge?

a) $\int_1^\infty \frac{1}{x^4}dx$ b) $\int_1^\infty \frac{1}{\sqrt[3]{x}}dx$ c) $\int_1^\infty \frac{dx}{\sqrt{x+2}}$ d) $\int_1^\infty \frac{1}{x}dx$ e) None of the above

Answer: $\int_1^\infty \frac{1}{x^4}dx$

43. Evaluate: $\int_2^\infty x^{-3}dx$.

a) $-\frac{1}{8}$ b) $\frac{1}{64}$ c) $\frac{3}{8}$ d) $\frac{1}{8}$ e) None of the above

Answer: $\frac{3}{8}$

44. Evaluate: $\int_{-\infty}^{-2} \frac{2}{(x+1)^2}dx$.

a) 2   b) –2   c) $\frac{2}{3}$ d) 0   e) None of the above

Answer: 2

45. Find the area between the two curves $y = e^{-x}$ and $y = -e^{-x}$ for $x \geq 0$.

Answer: 2

46. Use integration by parts to determine whether the improper integrals converge or diverge. If they converge, state the value.

A. $\int\limits_{0}^{\infty} xe^{-x} dx$

   Answer: Converges to 1

B. $\int\limits_{-\infty}^{0} x^2 e^x dx$

   Answer: Converges to 2

47. Evaluate: $\int\limits_{0}^{\infty} 100e^{-0.01x} dx$

   Answer: 1000

48. Evaluate: $\int\limits_{-\infty}^{\infty} \frac{x}{(1+x^2)^2} dx$

   Answer: 0

49. Evaluate: $\int\limits_{-\infty}^{-1} x^{-2} dx$

   Answer: 1

50. Evaluate: $\int\limits_{1}^{\infty} 2x^{\frac{-1}{2}} dx$

   Answer: Does not exist

144

51. Evaluate: $\int_{3}^{\infty} \dfrac{dx}{(x+1)^3}\,dx$

Answer: $\dfrac{1}{32}$

52. Determine the value of the constant k such that $f(x) = \dfrac{k}{\sqrt{x-8}}$ is a probability density function on the interval [8, 24].

Answer: $\dfrac{1}{8}$

53. A study has been made of the customer phone calls coming into the switchboard of the Municipal Power Company between 8:00 AM and 12 noon on Monday mornings. The results show that the time a caller will wait on hold before being connected with a service representative is an exponentially distributed random variable x with an expected value of 44 seconds.

A. What is the probability that a customer phoning the power company on Monday will have to wait on hold less than 32 seconds? (Round answer to the nearest thousandth)

Answer: 0.517

B. What is the probability that a customer phoning the power company on Monday will have to wait on hold more than $1\frac{1}{4}$ minutes? (Round answer to the nearest thousandth)

Answer: 0.182

54. Integrate $\int \dfrac{(1-xe^{-x})}{(x-1)^2}\,dx$.

Answer: $\dfrac{e^{-x}-1}{x-1} + C$

55. Evaluate the definite integral $\int_{1}^{e} x\ln(x^2)\,dx$.

Answer: $\dfrac{e^2+1}{2}$

145

56. Use a table to evaluate $\int \dfrac{dx}{x\sqrt{1-x^2}}$.

Answer: $-\ln\left|\dfrac{1-\sqrt{1-x^2}}{x}\right| + C$

57. Use a table to evaluate $\displaystyle\int_{\frac{-1}{2}}^{1} x\sqrt{1+2x}\, dx$.

Answer: $\dfrac{2\sqrt{27}}{15}$

58. Determine the bounds on the error incurred when $\displaystyle\int_{0}^{3} e^x dx$ is approximated by the Trapezoidal Rule with $n = 10$.

Answer: 0.4519

59. Simpson's Rule is based on which basic premise?

a) Any three collinear points define a line that passes through a portion of the graph $y = f(x)$.
b) Portions of the graph of $y = f(x)$ can approximate a parabola.
c) Portions of second-degree polynomial graphs may approximate portions of the graph of $y = f(x)$
d) Any three non collinear points define a unique parabola that may approximate the graph $y = f(x)$ over the entire interval $[a, b]$.

Answer: c)

60. Evaluate $\displaystyle\int_{2}^{\infty} \dfrac{x}{x^2-1} dx$.

Answer: Divergent

61. Given $\int_{1}^{\infty} \frac{1}{x^n} dx$, determine the values of n that make the improper integral divergent.

   Answer: Divergent for $n \le 1$

63. Evaluate $\int_{0}^{\infty} \frac{1+\sqrt{x}}{\sqrt{x}} dx$.

   Answer: Divergent

64. Evaluate $\int_{e}^{\infty} \frac{dx}{x(\ln(x^2))^3}$.

   Answer: $\frac{1}{16}$

APPLIED CALCULUS

CHAPTER 8
CALCULUS OF SEVERAL VARIABLES

1. A division of Conglomco International manufactures both television sets with and without stereo sound systems. The estimated quantities of one particular model demanded monthly are x units with stereo and y units without stereo, when the corresponding unit prices, in dollars, are
    $p = 3360 - \frac{1}{3}x - \frac{1}{9}y$ and $q = 1440 - \frac{1}{21}x - \frac{8}{21}y$, Respectively.
    What is the monthly total revenue function $R(x,y)$?

    Answer: $-\frac{1}{3}x^2 - \frac{8}{21}y^2 - \frac{10}{63}xy + 3360x + 1440y$

2. Graph the level curves of $z = f(x,y) = -2x - 8y$ for $z = -8, 0, 3, 8$.

    Answer:

    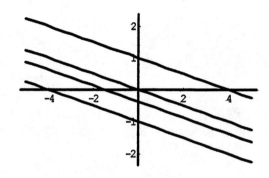

3. If $f(x,y) = 4x^2 - y^2 - 3xy^2$, find $f(-1,-2)$.

    a) -12 b) 20   c) 21   d) 12   e) None of the above

    Answer: 12

4. If $f(x,y) = 4x^2 - 3y^2 - 5xy^2$, find $f(-1,-2)$.

    a) 4   b) 12   c) 28   d) 36   e) None of the above

    Answer: 12

5. If $f(x,y) = 3x^4 - 4x^2y^3 + 2y^2$, find $f(0,1)$.

   Answer: 2

6. If $f(x,y) = 2x^4 - 5x^2y^3 + 3y^2$, find $f(0,1)$.

   Answer: 3

7. If $f(x,y) = 4x^2 - 3xy + 3y^2$, find $f(1,5)$.

   Answer: 64

8. If $g(x,y) = \ln(x^2 + y^2)$, find $g(3,9)$ to four decimal places.

   Answer: 4.4998

9. If $A(P,i,n) = P(1+i)^n$, find $A(5500, 0.12, 10)$ to the nearest hundredth.

   Answer: 17,082.17

10. If $V(l,w,h) = lwh$, find $V(25,8,4)$.

    Answer: 800

11. If $V(a,b,h) = \pi abh$, find $V(5,7,12)$.

    Answer: $420\pi \approx 1319$

12. Compute the first partial derivatives of $f(x,y) = x^4 - 4y^3 + 2xy$.

    Answer: $\frac{\partial f}{\partial x} = 4x^3 + 2y$; $\frac{\partial f}{\partial y} = -12y^2 + 2x$

13. Compute the first partial derivatives of $f(x,y) = x^2 \ln(x^2 + y^3)$.

    Answer: $\frac{\partial f}{\partial x} = 2x \ln(x^2 + y^3) + \frac{2x^3}{x^2 + y^3}$; $\frac{\partial f}{\partial y} = \frac{3x^2 y^2}{x^2 + y^3}$

149

14. Suppose that $f(x,y) = 3x^2 - 4x^2y - 2y^2$. Find $\frac{\partial f}{\partial x}$.

    a) $6x - 8xy$ b) $6x - 8xy - 4y$ c) $6x - 4x^2 + 8xy - 4y$
    d) $-2x$ e) None of the above

    <u>Answer:</u> $6x - 8xy$

15. Suppose that $f(x,y) = 5x^2 - 4x^2y - 2y^2$. Find $\frac{\partial f}{\partial x}$.

    a) $10x - 8xy$ b) $10x - 8xy - 4y$ c) $10x - 4x^2 + 8xy - 4y$
    d) $2x$ e) None of the above

    <u>Answer:</u> $10x - 8xy$

16. Let $f(x,y) = 3x^3 + 2y^2 - 4x^2y^2$. Find $f_{xx}(1,2)$.

    a) 14   b) -10 c) 6   d) -14 e) None of the above

    <u>Answer:</u> -14

17. Let $f(x,y) = 3x^3 + 6y^2 - 4x^2y^2$. Find $f_{xx}(1,2)$.

    a) 14   b) -2 c) 6   d) -14 e) None of the above

    <u>Answer:</u> -14

18. Suppose $f(x,y) = 3x^4 - 4x^2y^3 + 2y^2$.

A. Find f_x.

    <u>Answer:</u> $12x^3 - 8xy^3$

B. Find f_y.

    <u>Answer:</u> $-12x^2y^2 + 4y$

C.	Find f_{xy}.

Answer: $-24xy^2$

D.	Find $f_{xx}(0,1)$.

Answer: -8

19.	Suppose $f(x) = 6x^4 - 5x^2y^3 + 3y^2$.

A.	Find f_x.

Answer: $24x^3 - 10xy^3$

B.	Find f_y.

Answer: $-15x^2y^2 + 6y$

C.	Find f_{xy}.

Answer: $-30xy^2$

D.	Find $f_{xx}(0,1)$.

Answer: 72

20.	If $f(x,y) = e^{x^2+y^2}$, find f_x.

Answer: $2xe^{x^2+y^2}$

21.	If $g(x,y) = (3x-4y)^7$, find g_y.

Answer: $-28(3x-4y)^6$

22. If $z = F(x, y) = \dfrac{50}{x^2 + y^2}$, find $\dfrac{\partial z}{\partial x}$.

Answer: $-\dfrac{100x}{(x^2 + y^2)^2}$

23. If $f(x, y, \gamma) = 5xy + \gamma(5x + 3y - 250)$, find f_γ.

Answer: $5x + 3y - 250$

24. If $z = F(x, y) = \dfrac{5xy}{x + y}$, find $\dfrac{\partial z}{\partial x}$.

Answer: $\dfrac{5y^2}{(x + y)^2}$

25. If $f(x, y) = 2x^5 - 3x^2 y^2 + 3y^3 - 450$, find $f_{xx}(x, y)$.

Answer: $40x^3 - 6y^2$

26. If $f(x, y) = 2x^5 - 3x^2 y^2 + 3y^3 - 450$, find $f_{xx}(1, 2)$.

Answer: 16

27. If $f(x, y) = 2x^5 - 3x^2 y^2 + 3y^3 - 450$, find $\dfrac{\partial z}{\partial x \partial y}$.

Answer: $-12xy$

28. If $f(x, y) = 2x^5 - 3x^2 y^2 + 3y^3 - 450$, find $\dfrac{\partial^2 z}{\partial y^2}$.

Answer: $-6x^2 + 18y$

29. If $z = F(x, y) = \dfrac{5xy}{x + y}$, find $\dfrac{\partial^2 z}{\partial y^2}$.

Answer: $-\dfrac{10y^2}{(x + y)^3}$

30. Let $f(x,y) = 2y^3 - x^2 + 12y^2 + 4x - 30y + 15$.

A. Find the critical points, if any.

   Answer: $(2,1)$ and $(2,-5)$

B. State the results of applying the Second Derivative test at each critical point, naming any relative extrema.

   Answer: Relative maximum: $f(2,-5) = 219$; saddle point at $(2,1)$

31. Minimize the function $f(x,y) = 3x^2 + y^2 + 2$ subject to the constraint $x - y = 1$.

   Answer: $\frac{11}{4}$ at $\left(\frac{1}{4}, -\frac{3}{4}\right)$

32. Let $f(x,y) = \frac{2x - 5y^3}{xy^3}$.

A. Find the critical points, if any.

   Answer: No critical points

B. State the results of applying the Second Derivative Test at each critical point, naming any relative extrema.

   Answer: No critical points; Second Derivative Test not applicable

33. Use the Second Derivative Test to determine all possible relative maximum and minimum points of $f(x,y) = x^3 + 12y^2 - 12xy - 9x + 2$.

   Answer: $(3, 1.5, -25)$ is a relative minimum for f.

34. Consider the function $f(x,y) = 3x^2 + 3y^2 + 4xy - 8x + 4y + 2$. Find the critical points and then determine any relative maximum, relative minimum, or saddle points for the function.

   Answer: $\left(\frac{16}{5}, -\frac{14}{5}, -\frac{82}{5}\right)$ is a relative minimum for f.

35. A company produces two products and its revenue R in hundreds of dollars from selling x hundred units of one item and y hundred units of the other is given by:
$R(x,y) = -2x^2 - 20y^2 + 68x + 73y - 2xy.$

A. How many units of x and y must be sold to maximize the revenue?

Answer: 1650 units of x and 100 units of y

B. What is the maximum revenue?

Answer: $59,750

36. A company produces two products and its revenue R in hundreds of dollars from selling x hundred units of one item and y hundred units of the other is given by:
$R(x,y) = -8x^2 - 5y^2 + 39x + 39y - 2xy.$

A. How many units of x and y must be sold to maximize the revenue?

Answer: 200 units of x and 350 units of y

B. What is the maximum revenue?

Answer: $125,250

37. Find the relative extrema and saddle points for $f(x,y) = x^2 + y^2 - 10$.

Answer: Relative minimum at $(0,0,-10)$

38. Find the relative extrema and saddle points for $f(x,y) = 2x^3 - 6xy + y^3$.

Answer: Saddle point at $(0,0,0)$ and relative minimum at ($\sqrt[3]{2}$, $\sqrt[3]{4}$, -4)

39. Find the relative extrema and saddle points for $f(x,y) = \dfrac{1}{e^{x^2+y^2}}$.

Answer: Relative maximum at $(0,0,1)$

40. Find the relative extrema and saddle points for $f(x,y) = 2x^2 + 3xy - 5y^2 - 12x$.

Answer: Saddle point at $\left(\dfrac{120}{49}, \dfrac{36}{49}, -\dfrac{35280}{2401}\right)$

41. Find the relative maximum of $f(x,y) = 4 - x + 2y$ subject to $x^2 + y^2 = 9$.

Answer: $\left(\dfrac{-3\sqrt{5}}{5}, \dfrac{6\sqrt{5}}{5}, 4 + 3\sqrt{5}\right)$

42. Find the relative maximum of $f(x,y) = x^2 + y^2$ subject to $x - y - 4 = 0$.

Answer: $(2, -2, 8)$

43. Find two numbers whose product is a maximum subject to $x + y = 8$.

Answer: $x = y = 4$

44. Find two numbers whose product is a maximum subject to $x + y = 50$.

Answer: $x = y = 25$

45. Find the relative minimum of $f(x,y) = 4x^2 + 9y^2$ subject to $x + y - 4 = 0$.

Answer: Minimum of $\dfrac{576}{13}$ at $x = \dfrac{36}{13}$, $y = \dfrac{16}{13}$

46. Evaluate: $\displaystyle\int_2^4 \left(5x^4 - 2xy + y^3\right)dx$.

Answer: $2y^3 - 12y + 992$

47. Evaluate: $\displaystyle\int_{-3}^1 \left(x^2 + 2xy + y^3\right)dy$.

Answer: $4x^2 - 8x + \dfrac{28}{3}$

48. Evaluate: $\int_{1}^{e^2} x^{-1} y^3 \, dx$.

Answer: $2y^3$

49. Evaluate: $\int_{0}^{1} xy\sqrt{x^2 - y^2} \, dy$.

Answer: $\dfrac{x}{3}$

50. Evaluate: $\int_{2}^{4} (x + 2y)^2 \, dy$.

Answer: $2x^2 + 24x + \dfrac{224}{3}$

51. Evaluate: $\int_{0}^{2} \int_{0}^{4-2y} 3xy \, dx \, dy$.

Answer: 8

52. Evaluate: $\int_{0}^{4} \int_{0}^{(4-x)/2} 3xy \, dy \, dx$.

Answer: 16

53. Evaluate: $\int_{0}^{1} \int_{x^2}^{2x} (3y^2 + 2y + 6) \, dy \, dx$.

Answer: $\dfrac{734}{105} \approx 7$

156

54. Evaluate: $\displaystyle\int_1^5 \int_{(y-3)^2+1}^{5} 6\,dx\,dy$.

Answer: 64

55. Evaluate: $\displaystyle\int_1^3 \int_1^y (x+3y)\,dx\,dy$.

Answer: $17\frac{1}{3}$

56. Evaluate: $\displaystyle\int_0^1 \int_0^x xy\,dy\,dx$ by reversing the order of integration.

Answer: $\displaystyle\int_0^1 \int_y^1 xy\,dx\,dy = \frac{1}{8}$

57. Evaluate: $\displaystyle\int_0^4 \int_0^{\sqrt{y}} 3xy\,dx\,dy$ by reversing the order of integration.

Answer: $\displaystyle\int_0^2 \int_{x^2}^4 3xy\,dy\,dx = 32$

58. Evaluate: $\displaystyle\int_0^1 \int_{\sqrt{y}}^1 \sqrt{x^3+1}\,dx\,dy$ by reversing the order of integration.

Answer: $\displaystyle\int_0^1 \int_0^{x^2} \sqrt{x^3+1}\,dy\,dx = \frac{1}{2}$

59. Evaluate: $\displaystyle\int_0^1 \int_{e^x}^{e} \frac{1}{\ln y}\, dy\, dx$ by reversing the order of integration.

Answer: $\displaystyle\int_0^e \int_0^{\ln y} \frac{1}{\ln y}\, dx\, dy = e - 1$

60. Evaluate: $\displaystyle\int_1^3 \int_x^3 (x + 3y)\, dy\, dx$ by reversing the order of integration.

Answer: $17\frac{1}{3}$

61. Find the volume of the region defined by: $\displaystyle\iint_R x^2 y\, dx\, dy \begin{cases} 2 \le x \le 4 \\ 0 \le y \le 3 \end{cases}$.

Answer: 84

62. Find the volume of the region defined by: $\displaystyle\iint_R x^2 y\, dx\, dy \begin{cases} 2 \le x \le 3 \\ 2 \le y \le 4 \end{cases}$.

Answer: 54

63. Find the volume of the region defined by: $\displaystyle\iint_R (x^2 + xy - y^2)\, dA$ bounded by $y = x$ and $y = x^2$.

Answer: $\dfrac{47}{840}$

64. Find the volume of the region defined by: $\displaystyle\iint_R dA$ bounded by $y = 2x - 2$ and $(y - 1)^2 = 4x$.

Answer: 9

65. Find the volume of the solid bounded by the surface $z = x^2 + y^2$ about the region R: $1 \le x \le 2$, $2 \le y \le 4$.

Answer: $23\frac{1}{3}$

66. Reggie Construction estimates that the profit (in thousands of dollars) made on the construction of several buildings is $P(x,y) = -5 + 10x - x^2 + 6y - y^2$, where x is the number of projects in Miami and y is the number of construction projects in Tampa. How many construction projects in each city will yield the maximum profit?

Answer: 5 projects in Miami and 3 in Tampa

67. A feed lot manager wishes to provide her cattle with a supplement which will give 3000 gm of carbohydrates, 1500 gm of protein and 1800 gm of fat. Two feed supplements are commercially available. Each pound of the first provides 150 gm of carbohydrates, 30 gm of protein and 45 gm of fat. Each pound of the second contains 75 gm of carbohydrates, 75 gm of protein and 60 gm of fat. The first supplement costs \$4.35/lb., and the second costs \$2.25/lb. What combination of supplements should be purchased to minimize the cost?

Answer: For each 8# of the first, use 24# of the second

68. A furniture company has found that the labor cost, L, for the production of its finished furniture pieces is the following function of construction time, c, and finishing time, f: $L(c,f) = c^2 + 6cf + 10f^2 - 16c - 52f + 110$. Find the minimum labor cost and the number of hours of construction and finishing required.

Answer: Cost of \$42 for 2 hr. of construction and 2 hr. of finishing

69. Find the line of best fit for the following data points.

x	y
0	4
-2	0
1	5

a) $y = \frac{12}{7}x + \frac{25}{7}$

b) $y = 2x + 3$

c) $y = \frac{25}{7}x + \frac{12}{7}$

d) $y = \frac{12}{7}x - \frac{25}{7}$

e) None of the above

Answer: $y = \frac{12}{7}x + \frac{25}{7}$

159

70. Find the line of best fit for the following data points.

x	y
0	10
−2	4
2	12

a) $y = \frac{26}{3}x + 2$ b) $y = 2x + 8$ c) $y = 2x - \frac{26}{3}$

d) $y = 2x + \frac{26}{3}$ e) None of the above

Answer: $y = 2x - \frac{26}{3}$

71. Consider the following data:

x	y
−2	−1
−1	1
0	2
1	3
2	5

A. Find $f(m, b)$.

Answer: $(3 + 2m - b)^2 + (4 + m - b)^2 + (6 - b)^2 + (6 - m - b)^2 + (8 - 2m - b)^2$

B. Find $f_m(m, b)$.

Answer: $20m - 24$

C. Find $f_b(m, b)$.

Answer: $10b - 54$

72. Consider the following data:

x	y
2	5
4	10
6	12

A. Find $f(m, b)$.

Answer: $(5 - 2m - b)^2 + (10 - 4m - b)^2 + (12 - 6m - b)^2$

160

B.   Find $f_m(m, b)$.

Answer: $-244 + 112m + 24b$

C.   Find $f_b(m, b)$.

Answer: $24m + 6b - 54$

73.   Consider the following data:

x	y
2	5
4	10
6	12

Find the line of best fit.

Answer: $y = 1.75x + 2$

74.   Consider the following data:

x	y
-2	-1
-1	1
0	2
1	3
2	5

Find the line of best fit.

Answer: $y = 1.4x + 2$

75.   An entrance examination into a certain mathematics class is administered. At the end of the semester, the class grade is compared with their class standing, as shown on the following table:

Class Standing:	1	2	3	4	5	6	7	8	9	10
Entrance examination	85	80	90	70	80	50	60	65	50	45

Find the regression line.

Answer: $y = -4.58x + 92.67$

76. Compare IQ with achievement level in a certain English class

IQ	105	87	110	101	85	90
Class score	85	110	80	90	100	110

Find the regression line.

Answer: $y = -1.12x + 204.19$

77. Compare socioeconomic status with the time watching television, as given by the following table:

Status (rank)	1	2	3	4	5	6	7	8	9	10
TV time (rank)	2	1	3	5	4	7	6	10	9	8

Find the regression line.

Answer: $y = 0.85x + 0.6$

78. A large company did a study of the formal education level of its employees. They randomly selected 100 employees in each of 10 age classifications: 25-30, 30-35, ...,70-75, and found the mean number of years of education for that group. The following table summarized that data:

Age group:	1	2	3	4	5	6	7	8	9	10
Years education:	14.3	14.5	13.8	13.5	13.1	12.8	12.1	11.7	11.3	11.5

Find the regression line.

Answer: $y = -0.37939x + 14.947$

79. A study of the number of coronary attacks per 100 individuals, in various income groups gave the following data (income in thousands of dollars):

Income:	0-10	10-20	20-30	30-40	40-50	50-60	60-70	70-80	80-90	90-100
Attacks:	57	59	61	56	53	55	59	61	65	71

Find the regression line.

Answer: $y = 1.08484x + 53.73333$

80. At Frost Machine Tools, x units of labor and y units of capital are necessary to complete $f(x,y) = 110x^{3/4}y^{1/4}$ units of their product. The unit costs of labor and capital are $100 and $250, respectively, with a total of $120,000 allocated for production next quarter. Using the Method of Lagrange Multipliers, determine the number of units of labor and the number of units of capital that must be utilized in order to maximize quarterly production.

Answer: 900 units of labor; 120 units off capital

81. Evaluate the double integral for $f(x,y) = 6x^2 - 6xy^2 + 6y + 5$, where R is the rectangle defined by $-3 \le x \le -1$ and $-1 \le y \le 0$.

Answer: 64

82. Evaluate the double integral for $f(x,y) = 9y + 4$, where R is bounded by $x = -2$, $x - 2y = 1$, $y = 0$, and $y = 1$.

Answer: $\dfrac{71}{2}$

83. Evaluate the double integral for $f(x,y) = -6y$, where R is bounded by $y = \dfrac{2}{3}x$ and $y = \sqrt{4x}$.

Answer: -162

84. Evaluate the double integral for $f(x,y) = (y-1)^{-1/2}e^{2y}$, where R is bounded by the y-axis $x = 0$, the horizontal line $y = 5$, and $y = x^2 + 1$.

Answer: $\dfrac{e^2}{2}\left(e^8 - 1\right)$

85. Find the volume of the solid bounded above by the surface $z = f(x,y) = 3x^2 + 3y^2$ and below by the plane region defined by $y = \dfrac{1}{3}x$, $y = x$, and $y = 3$.

Answer: 648 cubic units

86. The population density of a certain college town is given by the function $f(x,y) = 9000e^{-0.2|x|-0.3|y|}$ where x and y are in miles and the origin gives the location of the center of the college campus. What is the population inside the rectangular area described by $D = \{(x,y)|\ 0 \le x \le 4,\ -7 \le y \le 7\}$, to the nearest whole number?

Answer: 144,971 people

87. Find the average value of $f(x,y) = x$ over the triangular plane region bounded by $y = 4x$, $y = 8 - 4x$, and the y-axis.

Answer: $\frac{1}{3}$

88. For the joint probability density function $f(x,y) = \frac{1}{16}xy$ ($0 \le x \le 2,\ 0 \le y \le 4$) associated with the random variables x and y, what is the probability that the observed values x and y lie in the region $D = \{(x,y)|\ 0 \le x \le 1, 0 \le y \le 0.2\}$? (Give the answer in decimal form, correct to ten-thousandths.)

Answer: 0.0006

89. Maximize $-3x^2 + 4xy + 16y^2$ subject to $x + 2y - 10 = 0$.

Answer: $1300\ (x = -30,\ y = 20)$

90. Maximize $x^2 - 32x + 4y^2 + 256$ subject to $x + 4y - 26 = 0$.

Answer: $20\ (x = 18,\ y = 2)$

91. Find the domain of $f(x,y) = \left(\dfrac{x^2+y^2}{x^2-y^2}\right)\dfrac{x}{\ln x}$.

Answer: The set of points in the xy plane not containing the lines $x = 1$, $y = x$, and $y = -x$.

92. The semi-perimeter of a triangle is given by the function $S(a,b,c) = \frac{1}{2}(a+b+c)$. Where a,b,c are the three sides of the triangle. $A(S,a,b,c) = \sqrt{S(S-a)(S-b)(S-c)}$ is the area of a triangle where S is the semi-perimeter. Compute the semi-perimeter and the area of a triangle with sides $a=3$, $b=4$, $c=5$.

Answer: $S=6$, $A=6$

93. Find the real domain of $g(s,t) = \ln(st\sqrt{st-1}\,)$.

Answer: All real values of s and t such that $st \geq 1$.

94. Find $\frac{\partial f}{\partial u}$ and $\frac{\partial f}{\partial v}$ of the following:

A. $f(u,v) = e^{\frac{u}{v}}$

Answer: $\frac{\partial f}{\partial u} = \frac{e^{\frac{u}{v}}}{v}$; $\frac{\partial f}{\partial v} = \frac{-u}{v^2}e^{\frac{u}{v}}$

B. $f(u,v) = ue^{u+v}$

Answer: $\frac{\partial f}{\partial u} = (1+u)e^{u+v}$; $\frac{\partial f}{\partial v} = ue^{u+v}$

95. Compute the first partial derivative of $f(x,y,z) = \sqrt{x^2 + y^2 + z^2}$ with respect to z.

Answer: $f_z = \dfrac{z}{\sqrt{x^2+y^2+z^2}}$.

96. Find f_{zz} for $f(x,y,z) = e^{x^2+y^2+z^2}$.

Answer: $2(2z^2+1)e^{x^2+y^2+z^2}$

97. Find all second order partials of $f(x,y) = x\ln y + y\ln x$.

Answer: $f_{xx} = -\frac{1}{x^2}$; $f_{xy} = \frac{1}{y}$; $f_{yx} = \frac{1}{x}$; $f_{yy} = -\frac{1}{y^2}$

98. Apply the second derivative test to determine all relative extrema and saddle points of $f(x,y) = -\frac{x^3}{3} + yx + \frac{y^3}{3}$.

Answer: Saddle point at $(0, 0)$; Relative minimum at $(-1, 1)$.

99. Use the method of Lagrange multipliers to minimize the material needed to construct a rectangular box with a volume of 125 cubic units. What are the dimensions of the box?

Answer: $x = 5$, $y = 5$, $z = 5$

100. Big Barrel Co. wants to make the largest barrel possible that is light enough to be lifted by a worker. Big Barrel determines a barrel may not exceed 24π square units of material. Use Lagrange multipliers to find the maximum volume of a right circular cylinder that can be made from 24π square units of sheet metal.

Answer: 16π

101. Given the data points (x_1, y_1), (x_2, y_2), and (x_3, y_3) write the normal equations for the Method of Least Squares.

Answer: $\left((x_1)^2 + (x_2)^2 + (x_3)^2\right)m + (x_1 + x_2 + x_3)b = x_1 y_1 + x_2 y_2 + x_3 y_3$
$(x_1 + x_2 + x_3)m + 3b = y_1 + y_2 + y_3$

102. Determine the maximum error in calculating the volume $V = \frac{1}{3}\pi r^2 h$ of a cone if the radius and height are measured to be $r = h = 10$ inches within 0.25 inches maximum error.

Answer: 25π

103. Find the approximate percent increase in volume of a rectangular box if the height is held constant and the width and depth are increased by 5%.

Answer: 10%

104. Evaluate $\iint\limits_R f(x,y)dA$ for $f(x,y) = xye^{x^2}e^{y^2}$ over the rectangle $0 \le x \le 1$ and $0 \le y \le 1$.

Answer: $\frac{1}{4}(e-1)^2$

105. Find the volume under the plane $x+y+z=3$ and the region bounded by the positive $x,y,$ and z- axes.

Answer: 4.5 square units.

106. The average value of a function $f(x,y)$ over the region R defined by $y = \sqrt{100-x^2}$ and $-10 \le x \le 10$ is 348. What is the solid bounded above by $z = f(x,y)$ and the region R.

Answer: 17400π cubic units.

APPLIED CALCULUS

CHAPTER 9
DIFFERENTIAL EQUATIONS

1. Find the general solution for $\frac{dy}{dx} = y^2(2x-1)$.

   a) $-\frac{1}{y} = x^2 - x + C$

   b) $-\frac{y^3}{3} = x^2 - x + C$

   c) $-\frac{2}{y^3} = x^2 + C$

   d) $y = \frac{y^3}{3}(x^2 - x) + C$

   e) None of the above

   Answer: $-\frac{1}{y} = x^2 - x + C$

2. Find the general solution for $\frac{dy}{dx} = \frac{2y}{x^2}$.

   a) $\ln|y| = -\frac{4}{x^3} + C$

   b) $-\frac{1}{y^2} = -\frac{4}{x^3} + C$

   c) $-\frac{1}{y^2} = -\frac{2}{x}C$

   d) $\ln|y| = -\frac{2}{x} + C$

   e) None of the above

   Answer: $\ln|y| = -\frac{2}{x} + C$

3. Find the general solution for $y^3\frac{dy}{dx} + 2x = 3$.

   Answer: $y^4 = 12x - 4x^2 + C$

4. Find the general solution for $4x - y^2\frac{dy}{dx} + 1 = 0$.

   Answer: $y^3 = 6x^2 + 3x + C$

5. Find the particular solution to $y\frac{dy}{dx} = x^2 - 4$ given that $y = 4$ when $x = 0$.

   Answer: $3y^2 = 2x^3 - 24x + 48$

6. Find the particular solution to $x^3 \frac{dy}{dx} = y + 3$ given that $y = -2$ when $x = 1$.

Answer: $\ln|y + 3| = \frac{x^2 - 1}{2x^2}$

7. You are given the differential equation: $y' - 8x^3 y = 0$.

A. Show that $y = Ce^{2x^4}$ is a general solution of the differential equation.

Answer: $y' = C\left(8x^3 e^{2x^4}\right)$ and $y' - 8x^3 y = C\left(8x^3 e^{2x^4}\right) - 8x^3\left(Ce^{2x^4}\right) = 0$

B. Find a particular solution to the differential equation satisfying the side condition: $y(1) = \frac{1}{3}$.

Answer: $y = \frac{1}{3}e^{2(x^4 - 1)}$

8. Find the general solution for the following differential equation: $y' = \frac{6xy^4}{e^{x^2}(y^8 - 1)}$.

Answer: $3y^5 + \frac{5}{y^3} = -45e^{-x^2} + C$

9. Find the general solution for the following differential equation: $5y^2 + xyy' = -45$.

Answer: $x^{10}(y^2 + 9) = C$

10. Given $2x^2 y \frac{dy}{dx} + x^3 = 0$, find the particular solution given that the curve passes through the point $(-2, 2)$.

a) $x^2 + 2y^2 = 12$ b) $y^2 = -\frac{x^2}{2} + 4$ c) $y^2 = -\frac{x^2}{2} + 2$

d) $2y^2 = 6 - x^2$ e) None of the above

Answer: $x^2 + 2y^2 = 12$

11. Given $x^3 y \frac{dy}{dx} + y^2 = 0$, find the particular solution given that the curve passes through the point $(-1, 1)$.

a) $\frac{x^4 y^2}{8} + \frac{y^3}{3} - \frac{11}{24} = 0$ b) $-\frac{y^2}{2} = \frac{x^4}{4} - \frac{3}{4}$ c) $\ln|y| = \frac{1}{2x^2} - \frac{1}{2}$

d) $\ln|y| = \frac{1}{3x^2} - \frac{1}{3}$ e) None of the above

Answer: $\ln|y| = \frac{1}{2x^2} - \frac{1}{2}$

12. The rate at which a new employee can produce units on an assembly line is proportional to the difference between the maximum number of units (80) and the number of units (x) produced per day. Find a differential equation describing this relationship.

a) $\frac{dx}{dt} = k(x - 80)$ b) $\frac{dx}{dt} = k(80 - x)$ c) $\frac{dx}{dt} = x(80 - x)$

d) $\frac{dx}{dt} = 80 - kx$ e) None of the above

Answer: $\frac{dx}{dt} = x(80 - x)$

13. Find the equation of f given that: (1) the slope of the tangent line to the graph of f at any point $P(x,y)$ is given by the expression $\frac{dy}{dx} = -5x^3$; and (2) the graph of f passes through the point $\left(1, \frac{1}{12}\right)$.

Answer: $y = -\frac{5}{4}x^4 + \frac{4}{3}$

14. A certain fungus has been found to thrive on the filters of the climate-control system in a certain building when a constant temperature of $70^o F$ is maintained within the building, with the growth rate of the fungus on a filter proportional to the number of fungi on that filter at any time t. If there were 800 fungi present initially on a sample filter from the building and 1500 fungi present 3 days later, how many fungi will be on the filter at the end of 12 days if the ideal temperature is maintained?

Answer: 9888 fungi

170

15.   By the time the local health department declared an outbreak of the Balinese flu to have reached the epidemic level, 4 percent of the 1000 children attending Enchantment Valley Elementary School had already contracted the virus. The rate at which the flu spreads is jointly proportional to the number of students who have the flu and the number of students who have not yet contracted the disease. If, in the next ten days, 14 percent of the children had contracted the flu, how many of the students had contracted the virus after another ten days?

Answer: 389 students

16.   A tank initially contains 10 gallons of pure water. Brine containing 4 pounds of salt per gallon flows into the tank at a rate of 3 gallons per minute and the well-stirred mixture flows out of the tank at the same rate. Find the amount of salt present in the tank:

A.   at any time t.

Answer: $40\left(1 - e^{-3t/10}\right)$ pounds

B.   at the end of 25 minutes.

Answer: $40\left(1 - e^{-15/2}\right)$ pounds is approx. 40 pounds

C.   in the long run.

Answer: 40 pounds

17.   Suppose that $2000 is deposited into an account. The account balance increases as it earns interest at 9% per year, compounded continuously. Find a differential equation describing this rate of change if A represents the amount of money in the account at any time t.

a) $\frac{dA}{dt} = 2000 + 0.09A$ b) $\frac{dA}{dt} = 90A$ c) $\frac{dA}{dt} = 0.09A$

d) $\frac{dA}{dt} = e^{0.09t}$ e) None of the above

Answer: $\frac{dA}{dt} = 0.09A$

18. Use Euler's Method with $n = 5$ to obtain an approximation of the initial value problem $y' = x - y + 1$, $y(0) = 1$ when $x = 0.5$. (Round answer to the nearest ten-thousandth if necessary.)

Answer: 1.0905

19. A biologist is conducting an experiment involving diseased cells which are increasing at an amount proportional to the amount present at any time t, where t is measured in hours. If there were 500 diseased cells present after 5 hours and there were only 150 cells present initially, predict how many diseased cells the experimenter can expect to find after 12 hours.

Answer: About 2698

20. The rate at which a radioactive material R decays is proportional to the amount present at any time t measured in years. If there were 800 grams present initially and 600 grams after 3 years, how many grams will be left after 8 years?

Answer: 371.5 grams

21. Solve: $\dfrac{dy}{dx} = 2xy + y$.

Answer: $Me^{x^2 + x}$

22. Solve: $\dfrac{dy}{dx} = 15x^2 y^3$.

Answer: $y^{-2} = -10x^3 + C$

23. Solve: $3yy' = x - 3$.

Answer: $y^2 = \frac{1}{3}x^2 - 2x + C$

24. Solve: $y^2 y' = e^{x+3}$.

Answer: $y^3 = 3e^{x+3} + C$

25. Solve: $y' = x^2 \sqrt{y}$.

Answer: $2\sqrt{y} = \frac{x^3}{3} + C$

26. Solve $\frac{dy}{dx} = x^2 y^{-1}$ for y if $y = 8$ when $x = 3$.

Answer: $y^2 = \frac{2}{3}x^3 + 46$

27. Solve $y' = 3x^2 - 4x + 5$ for y if $y = 3$ when $x = 0$.

Answer: $x^3 - 2x^2 + 5x + 3$

28. Solve $y' = 6xe^{3x^2+2}$ for y if $y = e^2$ when $x = 0$.

Answer: e^{3x^2+2}

29. Solve $\frac{dy}{dx} = \frac{x^2 y^3}{y^2 - 2y + 3}$ for y if $y = 1$ when $x = 0$.

Answer: $6\ln|y| + 12y^{-1} - 9y^{-2} = 2x^3 + 3$

30. Solve $3yy' = x - 3$ for y if $y = 2$ when $x = 3$.

Answer: $y^2 = \frac{1}{3}x^2 - 2x + 7$

31. Solve $y^2 y' = e^{x+3}$ for y if $y = e$ when $x = 1$.

Answer: $y^3 = 3e^{x+3} + e^3 - 3e^4$

32. Find $\int (5 - 3x)(2x - 1)^4 dx$ by using parts.

Answer: $\frac{1}{40}(2x - 1)^5(19 - 10x) + C$

33. Find $\int x\sqrt{6-x}\,dx$ by using parts.

Answer: $\frac{-2}{3}x(6-x)^{\frac{3}{2}} - \frac{4}{15}(6-x)^{\frac{5}{2}} + C$

34. Find $\int xe^{4x}\,dx$ by using parts.

Answer: $\frac{1}{4}xe^{4x} - \frac{1}{16}e^{4x} + C$

35. Find $\int (5x+3)e^{-4x}\,dx$ by using parts.

Answer: $\frac{-1}{4}(5x+3)e^{-4x} - \frac{5}{16}e^{-4x} + C$

36. Find $\int (\ln x)(x^2 + 4x - 5)\,dx$ by using parts.

Answer: $(\ln x)\left(\frac{x^3}{3} + 2x^2 - 5x\right) - \frac{x^3}{3} - x^2 + 5x + C$

37. If inflation over the past five years has averaged 4.5%, how long will it take (to the nearest year) for $100 to be worth what $10 is worth today?

Answer: 51 years

38. The growth rate for a certain population is given by $\frac{dP}{dt} = 10^{-5}P(L-P)$ where P is the population in t years, $L = 10,000$ is the limiting value. If the initial population is 100, find the population function.

Answer: $P(t) = \dfrac{10,000}{1+9900e^{-0.1t}}$

39. Newton's Law of Cooling states that the temperature T of a cooling object drops at a rate which is proportional to the difference $T - M$, where M is the constant temperature of the surrounding medium. Thus, $\frac{dT}{dt} = -k(T-M)$, where k is a positive constant depending on the object which is cooling. Solve this differential equation.

Answer: $T(t) = M(1 - e^{-kt})$

174

40. Suppose the marginal cost of producing x copies of a book is given by $C'(x) = 100x^{\frac{-1}{2}}$ and it is known that $C(0) = 85,000$. Find the cost (to the nearest dollar) of producing 25,000 books.

Answer: $116,623

41. A certain bacterial culture is growing at a rate proportional to the amount present. If the culture began with 500 bacteria and 5 hours later had grown to 1600, how many will there be in 24 hours?

Answer: $\approx 133,000$

42. Which of the following is a particular solution of the differential equation $2y'' - y' - y = 0$?

a) $y = 3e^{\frac{1}{2}x} + 2e^x$ b) $y = 5e^{-\frac{1}{2}x} - 7e^x$ c) $y = 2e^{-\frac{1}{2}x} - 7e^{-x}$
d) $y = 2x^2 + 3e^x$ e) None of the above

Answer: $y = 5e^{-\frac{1}{2}x} - 7e^x$

43. Let $y'' - y\left(\frac{x-2}{x}\right) = k$.

A. Find the particular solution of $y = cxe^{-x}$ that satisfies the condition $y''(0) = -8$.

Answer: $y = 4xe^{-x}$

B. Find the value of k that satisfies the differential equation $y' - y(x - 2x) = k$ for the particular solution found in A).

Answer: $k = 0$

44. A building with a 10 million cu. ft. air space is filled with smoke. The concentration of smoke is M/cu. ft. of air. Fresh air is being pumped in at a rate of 900 cu. ft./sec. A well mixed interior atmosphere is evacuated at ground level at the same rate. Find the time needed to remove 99.9% of the smoke by the means described. Express your answer in hours to the nearest tenth.

Answer: 21.3 hours

45. Write a differential equation that expresses the rate of accumulation as inversely proportional to A, the amount present.

   Answer: $\dfrac{dA}{dt} = \dfrac{k}{A}$

46. Find a particular solution to the differential equation $y' = \dfrac{(x-1)}{x^2}y$ subject to the condition $y(1) = 2e$.

   Answer: $y = 2xe^{\frac{1}{x}}$

47. Which of the following is not a separable differential equation?

   a) $\dfrac{dy}{dx} = x^2 y^2 + 100$ b) $y' = f(x)g(x)$

   c) $y' + y = x^2 + 1$ d) $\dfrac{1}{x}\dfrac{dx}{dt} = \dfrac{k}{y}\dfrac{dy}{dt}$

   Answer: a) and c)

48. Find a particular solution to the differential equation $\dfrac{yy'}{2} - e^x = x(x+2)e^x$ subject to the condition $y(0) = 2$.

   Answer: $y = 2\sqrt{(x^2 + 1)e^x}$

49. A small pond contains 1,000,000 gallons of fresh water. Brackish water containing $\dfrac{1}{100}$ lb. of salt per gallon is allowed to trickle into the pond at a rate of 10 gal/hour. The pond has an outlet that allows well mixed water to exit at the same rate. How many years will it take for the pond to be within 10% of the same salinity of the incoming water?

   Answer: ≈ 26.3 years

50. Two 50 gallon tanks are full of fresh water. The first tank receives brine containing 1 lb. of salt per gallon of water at a rate of 5 gal./min.. The second tank receives a well mixed flow from the first tank at the same rate. The second tank also discharges a well mixed flow at a rate of 5 gal./min. How many minutes does it take for tank two to reach the same concentration of tank one (within 1% of tank one). Round your answer to the nearest tenth.

Answer: 4.6 min.

APPLIED CALCULUS

CHAPTER 10
TAYLOR POLYNOMIALS AND INFINITE SERIES

1. Find the fourth Taylor polynomial of $f(x) = \frac{1}{x-2}$ at $x = 0$.

    <u>Answer:</u> $P_4(x) = \frac{-1}{2} - \frac{1}{4}x - \frac{1}{8}x^2 - \frac{1}{16}x^3 - \frac{1}{32}x^4$

2. Use four iterations of Newton's method on an appropriate function $f(x)$ and initial guess $x_0 = 6$ to obtain an estimate of $\sqrt{26}$. (Round the answer to four decimal places.)

    <u>Answer:</u> 5.0990

3. You are given the sequence: 1, 8, 27, 64,... .

A. Find the general term.

    <u>Answer:</u> $a_n = n^3$

B. Discuss the convergence. If the sequence converges, find its limits.

    <u>Answer:</u> Diverges

4. Express the repeating decimal 1.57575757... as a rational number.

    <u>Answer:</u> $\frac{52}{33}$

5. Find the radius of convergence and the interval of convergence for the power series:
    $\sum_{n=0}^{\infty} \frac{(x+2)^n}{2^n}$.

    <u>Answer:</u> $R = 2; \; (-4, 0)$

6. Given the Taylor series, $\frac{1}{1-x} = 1 + x + x^2 + \ldots + x^n + \ldots, -1 \le x \le 1$, find the Taylor series and the interval of convergence for $f(x) = \frac{1}{2x-9}$ at $x = 0$.

Answer: $f(x) = -\frac{1}{9} - \frac{2}{9^2}x - \frac{2^2}{9^3}x^2 - \ldots - \frac{2^n}{9^{n+1}}x^n - \ldots; \left(-\frac{2}{9}, \frac{2}{9}\right)$

7. Given the Taylor series, $\ln(1+x) = x - \frac{1}{2}x^2 + \frac{1}{3}x^3 - \ldots + \frac{(-1)^{n+1}}{n}x^n + \ldots$, differentiate to find the Taylor series for $f(x) = \frac{1}{36x^2+1}$ at $x = 0$.

Answer: $f(x) = 2\left(6^2x - 6^4x^3 + 6^6x^5 - \ldots + (-1)^{n+1}6^{2n}x^{2n-1} + \ldots\right)$

8. Use a fourth-degree Taylor polynomial to approximate $\int_0^{0.3} (1+x^2)^{-\frac{1}{5}}\,dx$ to the nearest ten-thousandth.

Answer: 0.2983

9. Use the fourth Taylor Polynomial to approximate the function: $f(x) = 2e^{2x}$ at $x = 0$.

Answer: $P_4(x) = 2 + 4x + 4x^2 + \frac{8}{3}x^3 + \frac{4}{3}x^4$

10. Use the third Taylor Polynomial of $f(x) = \sqrt{x}$ at $x = 4$ to approximate $\sqrt{4.2}$. Leave your answer in the form of a fraction of two numbers.

Answer: $\frac{1049.288}{512}$

11. Write the first five terms of the following sequences:

A. $\{a_n\} = \left\{\frac{1}{n}\right\}$

Answer: $1, \frac{1}{2}, \frac{1}{3}, \frac{1}{4}, \frac{1}{5}$

B. $\{a_n\} = \left\{\dfrac{n+1}{n!}\right\}$

   Answer: $2, \dfrac{3}{2}, \dfrac{2}{3}, \dfrac{5}{24}, \dfrac{1}{20}$

C. $\{a_n\} = \left\{\dfrac{(-1)^n}{(2n)!}\right\}$

   Answer: $\dfrac{-1}{2!}, \dfrac{1}{4!}, \dfrac{-1}{6!}, \dfrac{1}{8!}, \dfrac{-1}{10!}$

D. $\{a_n\} = \left\{\dfrac{(-1)^{n-1}}{n^2}\right\}$

   Answer: $1, \dfrac{-1}{4}, \dfrac{1}{9}, \dfrac{-1}{16}, \dfrac{1}{25}$

12. Determine whether the sequence $\{a_n\}$ converge or diverge.

A. $a_n = \dfrac{(-1)^n}{n!}$

   Answer: Converges to 0

B. $a_n = \dfrac{5^n}{n}$

   Answer: Diverges

C. $a_n = \dfrac{n(n+1)}{n^3}$

   Answer: Converges to 0

D. $a_n = \dfrac{n}{\sqrt{n^2+2}}$

   Answer: Converges to 1

13. Find the general terms of each of the sequences.

A. $\dfrac{-1}{2}$, 4, $\dfrac{-1}{6}$, 8, ...

Answer: $(-1)^n(2n)^{(-1)^n}$

B. $\dfrac{100}{101}$, $\dfrac{101}{102}$, $\dfrac{102}{103}$, $\dfrac{103}{104}$, ...

Answer: $\dfrac{99+n}{100+n}$

C. $\dfrac{2\cdot3\cdot4}{2+3+4}$, $\dfrac{3\cdot4\cdot5}{3+4+5}$, $\dfrac{4\cdot5\cdot6}{4+5+6}$, $\dfrac{5\cdot6\cdot7}{5+6+7}$, ...

Answer: $\dfrac{(n+1)(n+2)(n+3)}{3n+6}$

D. $\dfrac{-\pi}{3}$, $\dfrac{3\pi}{5}$, $\dfrac{-5\pi}{7}$, $\dfrac{7\pi}{9}$, ...

Answer: $\dfrac{(-1)^n\pi(2n-1)}{2n+1}$

14. Determine if the given infinite series diverges or converges. If the series is convergent, find its sum.

A. $\displaystyle\sum_{n=0}^{\infty} \dfrac{1}{(n+4)(n+5)}$

Answer: Converges to $\dfrac{1}{4}$

B. $\displaystyle\sum_{n=0}^{\infty} (-3)^{n+1}$

Answer: Diverges

15. Find the sum of the geometric series if it exists.

A. $\displaystyle\sum_{n=0}^{\infty} \frac{6-3^n}{2^n}$

   Answer: Diverges

B. $\displaystyle\sum_{n=0}^{\infty} \frac{6(3^n)-2^n}{4^n}$

   Answer: 22

16. Find a rational number that has the repeated decimal representation shown below.

A. 0.123456789...

   Answer: $\dfrac{123456789}{10^9-1}$

B. 0.9999....

   Answer: 1

17. Find the radius of convergence and interval of convergence for the power series:

$$\sum_{n=0}^{\infty} \frac{n!(x-1)^n}{2^n}$$

   Answer: Converges only at the point $x = 1$.

18. Find the power series representation for $f(x) = e^{2(x+1)}$ about $x = 0$. Determine its interval of convergence.

   Answer: $\displaystyle\sum_{n=0}^{\infty} \frac{e^2 2^n x^n}{n!}$; $(-\infty, \infty)$

19. Find the power series representation for $f(x) = b^x$ about $x = 0$. Determine its interval of convergence.

Answer: $\displaystyle\sum_{n=0}^{\infty} \frac{(x \ln b)^n}{n!}$; $(-\infty, \infty)$

20. Find the power series representation for $f(x) = x^2 e^{x^2}$. Use $e^x = 1 + x + \frac{x^2}{2!} + \frac{x^3}{3!} + \dots + \frac{x^n}{n!} + \dots$ $(-\infty < x < \infty)$.

Answer: $\displaystyle\sum_{n=0}^{\infty} \frac{x^{2(n+1)}}{n!}$; $(-\infty, \infty)$

21. Find the fifth Taylor polynomial of $f(x) = x^3 e^{2x^7}$ about $x = 0$. Use this result to approximate $\displaystyle\int_0^1 f(x)dx$ to four decimal places. Use $e^x = \displaystyle\sum_{n=0}^{\infty} \frac{x^n}{n!}$.

Answer: 0.6239

22. Given $\frac{1}{1-x} = 1 + x + x^2 + x^3 + \dots + x^n + \dots$ $(-1 < x < 1)$, differentiate to find $f(x) = \frac{-1}{(1-3x)^2}$ about $x = 0$.

Answer: $f(x) = 1 + 6x + 27x^2 + 1108x^3 + \dots + n(3x)^{n-1} + \dots +$; $\left(\frac{-1}{3} < x < \frac{1}{3}\right)$

APPLIED CALCULUS

CHAPTER 11
TRIGONOMETRIC FUNCTIONS

1. Convert -405° to radian measure.

    Answer: $\frac{-9\pi}{4}$ radians

2. Convert $\frac{10}{3}\pi$ radians to degree measure.

    Answer: 600°

3. Evaluate: $\cos\frac{\pi}{4}$.

    Answer: $\frac{\sqrt{2}}{2}$

4. Find all values of θ that satisfy the equation: $\cos\theta = \frac{1}{2}$ over the interval $[0, 2\pi]$.

    Answer: $\frac{\pi}{3}, \frac{5}{3}\pi$

5. Sketch the graph of : $y = -2\cos 3x$.

    Answer:

    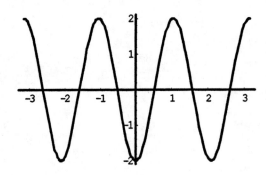

6. Find the derivative of the function: $f(x) = \sec^2 x \sin x$.

    Answer: $\sec x \tan^2 x + \sec^3 x$

7. Find the equation of the tangent line to the graph of the function: $f(x) = \sec x$ at the point $\left(\frac{\pi}{4}, \sqrt{2}\right)$.

Answer: $y = \sqrt{2}\, x - \dfrac{\pi}{2\sqrt{2}} + \sqrt{2}$

8. The height of a pier over the water level on a particular day is given by $h = 28 + 8\cos\dfrac{4\pi(t-5)}{23}$ feet, where $t = 0$ corresponds to 12 midnight. Determine the times of high and low tide for that day.

Answer: High tide at 5:00 a.m. and 4:30 p.m.; low tide at 10:45 a.m. and 10:15 p.m.

9. Evaluate the integral: $\int \sec^2 x \sin x\, dx$.

Answer: $\sec x + C$

10. The number of bees on a beehive during the month of April is given by the expression $N = 10,000 - 9000\cos\dfrac{2\pi(t-1)}{64}$, where t is in days and $t = 1$ corresponds to April 1st. Determine the average number of bees on the beehive for the week between the 9th and 16th of April.

Answer: 13,773

11. Convert each of the following angles to radian measure. Express the answer as a positive angle.

A. 60°

Answer: $\dfrac{\pi}{3}$

B. -180°

Answer: π

C. -720°

Answer: 0

185

D.   45°

Answer: $\frac{\pi}{4}$

12.   Convert each of the following angles to degree measure. Express the answer as a positive angle.

A. $\frac{2\pi}{3}$

Answer: 120°

B. $-\frac{\pi}{2}$

Answer: 270°

C. $-\frac{7\pi}{4}$

Answer: 45°

D. 2π

Answer: 0° or 360°

13.   Determine the quadrant in which the following angles lie.

A. $\frac{5\pi}{4}$

Answer: III

B. $-\frac{2\pi}{3}$

Answer: III

C. $\dfrac{100\pi}{101}$

Answer: II

D. -0.45π

Answer: IV

14. Evaluate the expression and leave your answer in fractional form.

A. $\cos\left(\dfrac{-\pi}{6}\right)$

Answer: $\dfrac{\sqrt{3}}{2}$

B. $\sin(45^{\circ})$

Answer: $\dfrac{\sqrt{2}}{2}$

C. $\sec\left(\dfrac{-4\pi}{3}\right)$

Answer: -2

D. $\cot(\pi)$

Answer: Undefined

15. Find all values of θ that satisfy the equation $\sin(-\theta) = -\cos\theta$ for $0 \le \theta \le 2\pi$.

Answer: $\theta = \dfrac{\pi}{4}, \dfrac{5\pi}{4}$

16. Simplify the identity $\dfrac{\tan\theta + \cot\theta}{\csc\theta}$.

Answer: $\sec\theta$

17. Choose the best value for A if $A = 1 - 2\sin^2\theta - \cos(2\theta)$.

 a) $\cos^2\theta - 1$
 b) $2\cos(2\theta)$
 c) 0
 d) $1 - \cos(2\theta)$

Answer: c)

18. Find the derivative of the function $f(x) = e^{\sin x}\csc x^2$.

Answer: $f'(x) = \cos x e^{\sin x} - 2x\csc x^2 \cot x^2$

19. Find $f''(\theta)$ if $f(\theta) = \sin^2\theta \cdot \cos^2\theta$.

Answer: $f''(x) = 2\cos(4\theta) = 2\sin^4\theta - 12\sin^2\theta\cos^2\theta + 2\cos^4\theta$

20. Find $f''(x)$ if $f(x) = x^2 e^{2\sin^2 x} e^{2\cos^2 x}$.

Answer: $2e^2$

21. Find the equation of the tangent line to the curve $f(x) = \cos x \sin^3 x + 2$ at $x = \dfrac{5\pi}{6}$.

Answer: $y = \dfrac{1}{2}x + \left[\dfrac{96 - 3\sqrt{3} - 20\pi}{48}\right]$

22. Find the intervals of increasing/decreasing, points of inflection, relative extrema, and concavity for $f(x) = e^x \sin x$ over the interval $[0, 2\pi]$.

Answer: Increasing on $\left(0, \dfrac{3\pi}{4}\right) \cup \left(\dfrac{7\pi}{4}, 2\pi\right)$; Decreasing on $\left(\dfrac{3\pi}{4}, \dfrac{7\pi}{4}\right)$;
  Relative max at $\left(\dfrac{3\pi}{4}, \dfrac{\sqrt{2}}{2}e^{\frac{3\pi}{4}}\right)$; Relative min at $\left(\dfrac{7\pi}{4}, \dfrac{-\sqrt{2}}{2}e^{\frac{7\pi}{4}}\right)$;
  Points of inflection $\left(\dfrac{\pi}{2}, e^{\frac{\pi}{2}}\right), \left(\dfrac{3\pi}{2}, -e^{\frac{3\pi}{2}}\right)$;
  Concave up on $\left(0, \dfrac{\pi}{2}\right) \cup \left(\dfrac{3\pi}{2}, 2\pi\right)$;
  Concave down on $\left(\dfrac{\pi}{2}, \dfrac{3\pi}{2}\right)$

23. Evaluate $\int_0^{\frac{\pi}{2}} \cos^4 x \sin x\, dx$.

Answer: $\dfrac{1}{5}$

24. Evaluate the indefinite integral $\int \cot^2 x\, dx$.

Answer: $-\cot x - x + C$

25. Evaluate the indefinite integral $\int \dfrac{\sin^2 x}{1 + \cot^2 x}\, dx$.

Answer: $\dfrac{3}{8} x - \dfrac{1}{4} \sin 2x + \dfrac{1}{32} \sin 4x + C$

Chapter Tests

Name_____

Section_____

1. Evaluate for $x = 16: x^{\frac{-3}{4}}$.

   Answer: _____

2. Solve for x: $2x - \pi \geq 3x + \sqrt{7}$.

   Answer: _____

3. Solve for x: $(2 - 3x)(x + 4) = 0$.

   Answer: _____

4. Multiply and simplify: $(x - 3)(x^2 - x - 2)$.

   a) $x^3 - 4x^2 + x + 6$ b) $x^3 - 3x^2 + x - 6$

   c) $x^3 - 4x^2 - 5x + 6$ d) $x^3 - 4x^2 + x - 6$

   Answer: _____

5. Solve for x: $\dfrac{2}{\sqrt{x}} - 3 = 0$.

   a) $\dfrac{2}{3}$ b) $\dfrac{9}{4}$ c) $\dfrac{3}{2}$ d) $\dfrac{4}{9}$

   Answer: _____

6. Solve for x: $3x^2 - 8 = 0$.

   a) $\dfrac{\pm\sqrt{8}}{3}$ b) $\dfrac{\pm 2\sqrt{3}}{3}$ c) $\dfrac{\pm 2\sqrt{6}}{3}$ d) $\dfrac{\pm 4\sqrt{2}}{3}$

   Answer: _____

7. Multiply each pair of given expressions.

A. $(2 + 3x)^2$

Answer: _____

B. $(1 + 3x)^2$

Answer: _____

8. Multiply each pair of given expressions.

A. $(x - 4y)(2x - y)$

Answer: _____

B. $(2x - 3y)(x + 4y)$

Answer: _____

9. Multiply each pair of given expressions.

A. $(3x + 5)(5x - 12)$

Answer: _____

B. $\left(3x^2 + 2y\right)\left(2x^2 - 5y\right)$

Answer: _____

10. Factor: $91x^2 - 246x + 143$.

Answer: _____

11. Find an equation of the line through $(0, 5)$ and parallel to the line $x + y - 5 = 0$.

a) $y = x + 5$ b) $y = x - 5$
c) $x + y + 5 = 0$ d) $x + y - 5 = 0$

Answer: _____

12. Find the point of intersection of the two lines $y = 1 - 2x$ and $x - y - 5 = 0$.

Answer: _____

13. Find the slope of the line passing through $\left(\frac{1}{2}, \frac{3}{2}\right)$, $\left(-\frac{2}{3}, \frac{1}{5}\right)$.

Answer: _____

14. Find the general form of the equation of the line passing through $(125, 400)$ and $(200, -50)$.

Answer: _____

15. A rental car has a base cost plus a cost per mile. If it costs $60 to drive it 100 miles, and $104 to drive it 500 miles, what will be the cost for 420 miles?

Answer: _____

Name_____

Section_____

1. Rationalize the denominator: $\dfrac{x}{2\sqrt{x}}$.

    a) $\dfrac{\sqrt{x}}{2}$ b) $\dfrac{\sqrt{x}}{4}$ c) $\dfrac{x\sqrt{x}}{2}$ d) $\dfrac{x}{4}$

    Answer: _____

2. Solve for x: $1 - 3x < -10$.

    Answer: _____

3. Solve for x: $-7 \le 10 - 2x \le -1$.

    Answer: _____

4. Rationalize the numerator: $\dfrac{\sqrt{x}}{\sqrt{x}+1}$.

    a) $\dfrac{x-\sqrt{x}}{x-1}$ b) $\dfrac{x}{x+\sqrt{x}}$ c) $\dfrac{1}{1+\sqrt{x}}$ d) $\dfrac{x}{x+1}$

    Answer: _____

5. Factor the following expression completely and leave all exponents positive in the answer.
    $$4x^2\left(x^2+1\right)^{\frac{-1}{2}} + 4\left(x^2+1\right)^{\frac{1}{2}}$$

    Answer: _____

6. Solve for x: $\dfrac{2}{\sqrt{x}} - 3 = 0$.

    a) $\dfrac{2}{3}$ b) $\dfrac{9}{4}$ c) $\dfrac{3}{2}$ d) $\dfrac{4}{9}$

    Answer: _____

7. Solve for x: $2x^2 + 2x - 1 = 0$.

 a) $\dfrac{-1 \pm 2\sqrt{3}}{2}$ b) $-1 \pm \sqrt{3}$

 c) $\dfrac{1 \pm \sqrt{3}}{2}$ d) $\dfrac{-1 \pm \sqrt{3}}{2}$

 Answer: _____

8. Multiply each pair of given expressions.

A. $(2 + 3x)^2$

 Answer: _____

B. $(1 + 3x)^2$

 Answer: _____

9. Multiply each pair of given expressions.

A. $(3x + 5)(5x - 12)$

 Answer: _____

B. $(3x^2 + 2y)(2x^2 - 5y)$

 Answer: _____

10. Factor: $6 - 7x - 3x^2$.

 Answer: _____

11. Solve for x: $3(x - 4) + 7(2x + 3) = 5(x - 2) - 4(3x + 5)$.

 Answer: _____

12. Find the $x-$ and $y-$intercepts for $10-x=4y$.

Answer: _____

13. Find the slope of the line passing through $(-3,2)$, $(5,0)$.

Answer: _____

14. Find the slope of the line passing through $(-1,-4)$, $(-8,3)$.

Answer: _____

15. Find the general form of the equation of the line passing through $(125,400)$ and $(200,-50)$.

Answer: _____

Name_____

Section_____

1.   Evaluate for $x = -8 : x^{\frac{-2}{3}}$.

      Answer: _____

2.   Solve for x: $2 \le -x \le 16$.

      Answer: _____

3.   Solve for x: $-1 \le 1 - 2x \le 1$.

      Answer: _____

4.   Solve for x: $(x-5)(x+2) = 8$.

      Answer: _____

5.   Factor completely: $16 - x^4$.

      a) $(x^2+4)(x^2-4)$ b) $(x-2)(x+2)(x^2+4)$

      c) $(2-x)(2+x)(x^2+4)$ d) $(x^2+2x+4)(x^2-2x+4)$

      Answer: _____

6.   Multiply each pair of given expressions.

A. $(x-3)(x+5)$

      Answer: _____

B. $(4-x)(5-2x)$

      Answer: _____

7. Multiply each pair of given expressions.

A. $(2+3x)^2$

    Answer: _____

B. $(1+3x)^2$

    Answer: _____

8. Multiply each pair of given expressions.

A. $(x-4y)(2x-y)$

    Answer: _____

B. $(2x-3y)(x+4y)$

    Answer: _____

9. A salesperson for the Fintext Publishing Company earns a base salary of $125 per week plus a 7% commission on sales (S). The formula for computing a salesperson's gross pay (G) is given by: $G = 125 + 0.078S$. Find the gross pay if the total sales for a week are $850.

    Answer: _____

10. Find an equation of the line with slope -4 and passing through the point $(3,0)$.

    a) $4x - y - 12 = 0$ b) $4x + y - 12 = 0$
    c) $4x + y + 3 = 0$ d) $4x + y - 3 = 0$

    Answer: _____

11. Find the point where the line $x - 3y + 4 = 0$ crosses the y-axis.

    a) $\left(0, \frac{-3}{4}\right)$ b) $\left(0, \frac{3}{4}\right)$ c) $\left(0, \frac{-4}{3}\right)$ d) $\left(0, \frac{4}{3}\right)$

    Answer: _____

12. Find the x- and y- intercepts for $75x + 250y = 10,000$.

    Answer: _____

13. Find the x- and y- intercepts for $3x + 4y = 12$.

    Answer: _____

14. Find the slope of the line passing through $(-3, 2)$, $(5, 0)$.

    Answer: _____

15. Find the general form of the equation of the line passing through $\left(\frac{1}{2}, \frac{1}{3}\right)$ and $\left(\frac{1}{4}, \frac{3}{4}\right)$.

    Answer: _____

1. Sketch a graph of $y = |2x - 1|$.

   Answer:

2. Evaluate: $\lim\limits_{x \to 3} \left(3x^2 - 4\right)$.

   a) 77　　　　b) 5　　　　c) 23　　　　d) Does not exist　　e) None of the above

   Answer: _____

3. Find $\lim\limits_{x \to 5} \dfrac{x^2 - 2x - 15}{x - 5}$.

   Answer: _____

4. Find $\lim\limits_{x \to 0} \dfrac{x^2 - 5x + 6}{x^2 - x - 6}$.

   Answer: _____

5. Sociologists have determined that the population of a small town, $N(t)$, can be modeled by the formula: $N(t) = \dfrac{2000t^2 + 200}{2t^2 + 1}$, where t is measured in years. Determine the limit of this function as $t \to \infty$, which represents the upper limit of the town's population.

   Answer: _____

6. Does time, as given on a dial watch, describe a continuous or discontinuous function?

   Answer: _____

7. Find the instantaneous rate of change for $y = 2x^2 - 3x$ when $x = 1$.

   Answer: _____

8. Find the instantaneous rate of change for $y = 3x^2 + 9x + 27$ when $x = 0$.

Answer: _____

9. Find the derivative of $y = 5\sqrt{x}$ using the definition.

Answer: _____

10. Find the instantaneous rate of change for $f(x) = -2x^3$ at $x = 2$.

a) −16   b) −6   c) −24   d) −22   e) None of the above

Answer: _____

11. Suppose the position of an object at any time t is given by $s(t) = -16t^2 + 96t + 116$, where t is measured in seconds and $s(t)$ is measured in feet.

A. Find the average rate of change of its position over the time interval from $t = 1$ second to $t = 2$ seconds.

Answer: _____

B. Find the instantaneous rate of change at $t = 1.5$ seconds.

Answer: _____

12. Let $y = x - x^3$

A. Find an equation of the tangent line drawn to the curve y at the point $(1, 0)$.

Answer: _____

B. Draw the function and the tangent line.

Answer:

13. Find the slope of the line tangent to the curve $y = x^2$ at $(1, 1)$.

Answer: _____

14. Let $f(x) = 3 - 2x^2$.

A. Find $\dfrac{f(x+h) - f(x)}{h}$.

Answer: _____

B. Find $\displaystyle\lim_{h \to 0} \dfrac{f(x+h) - f(x)}{h}$.

Answer: _____

15. Find the average rate of change for $y = 2\sqrt{x}$ on the interval $x = 4$ to $x = 9$.

Answer: _____

Name_____

Section_____

1. Find the domain for the function whose equation is $y = \sqrt{4x + 8}$.

   a) $x \geq 0$ b) $x \geq -2$ c) $x \geq 2$ d) $x < \frac{1}{2}$ e) None of the above

   Answer: _____

2. For $f(x) = -x^2 - 4x + 8$, find $f(-2)$.

   a) 4   b) 20   c) –4   d) 12   e) None of the above

   Answer: _____

3. The total cost of producing x units of an item is given by the function
   $C(x) = 200 + 20x + 0.2x^2$, where $C(x)$ is measured in dollars. Determine the total cost of producing 100 items.

   Answer: _____

4. A distributor can supply 6000 items when the cost is \$250 but cannot supply any at a cost of \$50 or less. Assume the relationship is linear and the domain is [50, 300].

A. What is the supply equation?

   Answer: _____

B. The demand is 5000 items when the price is \$50 and only 2000 items if the price is \$200. What is the equilibrium point for which the supply and demand are the same?

   Answer: _____

5. Find $\lim\limits_{x \to \infty} \dfrac{5x^3 + 2x^2 - x + 55}{2 - 3x^3}$.

   Answer: _____

6. Find $\lim_{x \to 16} \frac{\sqrt{x}-4}{x-16}$.

    Answer: _____

7. Find $\lim_{x \to \infty} \frac{x^2-5x+6}{x^2-x-6}$.

    Answer: _____

8. For what value(s) of x is the function below discontinuous?

    $$f(x) = \begin{cases} \frac{x^2+1}{x^2-2}, & x < 1 \\ \frac{-12x}{x+5}, & x \geq 1 \end{cases}$$

    Answer: _____

9. Let $y = f(x) = 3x^2 + 8$.

A. Find the average rate of change of y with respect to x over the interval [1, 1.6].

    Answer: _____

B. Find the instantaneous rate of change of y at $x = 1$.

    Answer: _____

10. Find the average rate of change for $y = \frac{5}{\sqrt{x}}$ on the interval $x = 1$ to $x = 4$.

    Answer: _____

11. Find the instantaneous rate of change for $y = \frac{5}{\sqrt{x}}$ when $x = 1$.

    Answer: _____

12. Find the derivative of $y = x^3$ using the definition.

Answer: _____

13. Find the derivative of $y = 5\sqrt{x}$ using the definition.

Answer: _____

14. Let $y = x - x^3$

A. Find an equation of the tangent line drawn to the curve y at the point $(1, 0)$.

Answer: _____

B. Draw the function and the tangent line.

Answer:

15. Let $f(x) = 4 - x^2$.

A. Find $\dfrac{f(x+h) - f(x)}{h}$.

Answer: _____

B. Find $\lim\limits_{h \to 0} \dfrac{f(x+h) - f(x)}{h}$.

Answer: _____

Tan Applied Calculus
Examination 2C

Name_____

Section_____

1. For $f(x) = -x^2 + 7x - 3$, find $f(-2)$.

a) -13 b) 7 c) -21 d) -12 e) None of the above

Answer: _____

2. For $f(x) = -x^2 - 4x + 8$, find $f(-2)$.

a) 4 b) 20 c) -4 d) 12 e) None of the above

Answer: _____

3. The total cost of producing x units of an item is given by the function $C(x) = 300 + 5x + 0.1x^2$, where $C(x)$ is measured in dollars. Determine the total cost of producing 100 items.

Answer: _____

4. Let $f(x) = 2 - 3x$, evaluate $\frac{f(x+h) - f(x)}{h}$. Leave your answer in simplified form.

Answer: _____

5. Evaluate: $\lim\limits_{x \to 3} \frac{x^2 - 9}{2x - 6}$.

a) $\frac{9}{2}$ b) 0 c) 3 d) Does not exist   e) None of the above

Answer: _____

6. Find $\lim\limits_{x \to 1} \frac{x^2 + 3x + 2}{x^2 - 1}$.

Answer: _____

7. The number of fish in a certain lake is given by the function $N(t) = \dfrac{2000t^2 + 200}{2t^2 + 1}$, where t is measured in months. Determine the limit of this function as $t \to \infty$, which represents the upper limit of the town's population.

Answer: _____

8. Determine whether $f(x) = \dfrac{x^2 - 3x + 2}{x^2 - 8x + 12}$ is continuous on $[-5, 5]$. Give any points of discontinuity.

Answer: _____

9. Find the derivative of $y = x^3$ using the definition.

Answer: _____

10. Let $f(x) = x^3 - 3x$.

A. Find the average rate of change for f from $x = 0.9$ to $x = 1.1$.

Answer: _____

B. Find the instantaneous rate of change for f at $x = 1$.

Answer: _____

11. Suppose the position of an object at any time t is given by $s(t) = -16t^2 + 32t + 640$, where t is measured in seconds and $s(t)$ is measured in feet.

A. Find the average rate of change of its position over the time interval from $t = 1$ second to $t = 7$ seconds.

Answer: _____

B. Find the instantaneous rate of change at $t = 4$ seconds.

Answer: _____

12. For $f(x) = x^2 - 8x$, find $f'(x)$.

a) $2x - 8 + h$ b) $2x + 8$ c) $2x - 8$ d) $8 - 2x$ e) None of the above

Answer: _____

13. Let $f(x) = 4 - x^2$.

A. Find $\dfrac{f(x+h) - f(x)}{h}$.

Answer: _____

B. Find $\lim\limits_{h \to 0} \dfrac{f(x+h) - f(x)}{h}$.

Answer: _____

14. The Puroform Company, which produces furniture, has determined that the cost of producing x chairs is given by the function $C(x) = 0.02x^2 + 40x + 400$, where $C(x)$ is measured in dollars.

A. Find $C'(x)$.

Answer: _____

B. Find $C'(20)$.

Answer: _____

15.   Consider the graph of the function $y = f(x)$ shown below.

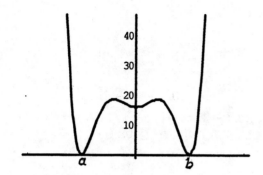

Which of the following statements are true?

i) $f(a) = f(b) = 0$
ii) $f'(a) = f'(b) = 0$
iii) $f'(x) \le 0$ if $a \le x \le c$

Answer: _____

1. Find the derivative of $y = -\dfrac{25}{x^2}$.

   Answer: _____

2. Find the derivative of $f(x) = -\dfrac{2}{3}x^4 + \sqrt{2}\,x^3 - 23x + 1005$.

   Answer: _____

3. If $y = \dfrac{1}{2x^2} + \dfrac{2}{x^3}$, find $\dfrac{dy}{dx}$.

   Answer: _____

4. Find the derivative of $f(x) = \left(3x^2 + 4x - 1\right)^3$.

   Answer: _____

5. Find the derivative of $f(x) = \left(3x^2 + 1\right)^4 (2 - 5x)^2$.

   Answer: _____

6. Find all derivatives of $y = 1 - 3x^4$.

   Answer: _____

7. Given $f(x) = 5x^3 - 4x^2 + 8x + 9$, evaluate $f''(x)$ when the slope of the tangent line to the graph of $f(x)$ is 8.

   Answer: _____

8. Let $y = \dfrac{2}{\sqrt{x}}$.

A. Find $\dfrac{dy}{dx}$.

   Answer: _____

B. Find $\dfrac{d^2y}{dx^2}$.

   Answer: _____

C. Find $\dfrac{d^3y}{dx^3}$.

   Answer: _____

9. Find $\dfrac{dy}{dx}$ for $x^2 + y^2 = 4x$.

   a) $\dfrac{4-x}{y}$ b) $\dfrac{x}{y}$ c) $\dfrac{2}{x+y}$ d) $\dfrac{2-x}{y}$ e) None of the above

   Answer: _____

10. A spherical hot air balloon is being filled. If the volume of the balloon is increasing at a rate of 40 ft^3/sec, at what rate is the radius increasing when the radius is 10 ft?

    Answer: _____

11. Find $\dfrac{dy}{dx}$ by using implicit differentiation: $x^2 + y^2 = 1$.

    Answer: _____

12. Find $\dfrac{dy}{dx}$ for $x^2 - xy + y^2 = 4$.

    Answer: _____

13. Find the slope of the line tangent to the curve $x^2 - 2xy + y^2 = 1$ at $(1,2)$.

Answer: _____

14. Approximate $\sqrt[3]{65}$ using differentials.

Answer: _____

15. If $y = 3\left(100 - x^{-3}\right)$, estimate the change in y when $x = 10$ and $\Delta x = 0.02$.

Answer: _____

Name_____

Section_____

1.   The Department of Fish and Game has planted a species of sunfish in a new man-made lake. They estimate the population (in thousands) at the end of t years to be given by $P(t) = 2t^3 + 3t^2 - 2t + 2$ for $0 \le t \le 5$.

A.   Find the growth rate at any time t.

Answer: _____

B.   Find the growth rate at the end of 4 years.

Answer: _____

2.   Find the equation of the line tangent to the curve $y = \frac{x}{x+1}$ at the origin.

a) $x + y = 0$ b) $x - y = 0$ c) $x - y + 1 = 0$
d) $x - y - 1 = 0$ e) None of the above

Answer: _____

3.   If $f(x) = \frac{1}{x^2+1}$, find $f'(2)$.

a) $\frac{1}{4}$ b) $-\frac{1}{25}$ c) $-\frac{4}{25}$ d) $\frac{1}{25}$ e) None of the above

Answer: _____

4.   A marine biologist is running experiments involving the environmental temperature for a particular species of fish. The appetite (A) of the fish seems to be affected by the temperature (T) of the water can be approximated by $A = \frac{5000}{T^2+1}$, $50^\circ \le T \le 80^\circ$, where $A = 1$ is considered normal appetite. Find the rate of change in appetite with respect to the temperature when the temperature is 60°.

Answer: _____

5. Find the derivative of $y = 6x^4(x^2 - 3x + 5)$.

Answer: _____

6. If $y = 1 - u^2$ and $u = \frac{1}{x}$, find $\frac{dy}{dx}$.

a) $\frac{2}{x^3}$ b) $\frac{2}{x}$ c) $-\frac{2}{x^3}$ d) $2x$ e) None of the above

Answer: _____

7. Find the derivative of $f(x) = (3x^2 + 1)^4(2 - 5x)^2$.

Answer: _____

8. Suppose that the demand equation for a certain product is given by $p = 115 - 0.2x$ and the cost is given by $C(x) = 1200 + 5x$.

A. Find $R(x)$.

Answer: _____

B. Find $P(x)$.

Answer: _____

C. Find $P'(x)$.

Answer: _____

9. If the profit, P in dollars, for a company is a function of the number of units produced, x, it can be determined that it approximates the function $P(t) = \frac{1000 - x^2}{5 - x^2}$. If the current level of production is 100 units, what is the per unit increase in profit if the production is increased from 100 to 110 units?

Answer: _____

214

10. Find the first four derivatives of $y = \frac{x-1}{2x^2}$.

Answer: _____

11. The equation of the unit circle (the circle centered at the origin of radius 1) is given by $x^2 + y^2 = 1$. Find the equation of the tangent line drawn to the point $\left(-\frac{\sqrt{2}}{2}, \frac{\sqrt{2}}{2}\right)$.

Answer: _____

12. Find $\frac{dy}{dx}$ if $(3x+4)^2 - (2y+3)^2 = 20$.

Answer: _____

13. Find the slope of the line tangent to the curve $(3x+4)^2 - (2y+3)^2 = 20$ at $(2,3)$.

Answer: _____

14. Let t change from 3 to 3.1 for $s = t^2$.

A. Find the actual change in s.

Answer: _____

B. Find the approximate change in s, dt.

Answer: _____

15. Find dy and Δy for $f(x) = \frac{2x-1}{x+2}$ when $x = 10$ and $\Delta x = 0.1$.

Answer: _____

Name_____

Section_____

1.   The Department of Fish and Game has planted a species of sunfish in a new man-made lake. They estimate the population (in thousands) at the end of t years to be given by $P(t) = 2t^3 + 3t^2 - 2t + 2$ for $0 \le t \le 5$.

A .   Find the growth rate at any time t.

Answer: _____

B.   Find the growth rate at the end of 4 years.

Answer: _____

2.   Find $g'(t)$ if $g(t) = \frac{2t+3}{t^2+1}$.

Answer: _____

3.   Find the derivative of $y = (3 - 5x)(x - 5)$.

Answer: _____

4.   If $f(x) = -2[g(x)]^4$, which expression represents $f'(x)$?

a) $-8[g(x)]^3 \cdot g'(x)$ b) $-8[g(x)]^3$ c) $4[-2g(x)]^3 \cdot g'(x)$
d) $-8\left[g'(x)\right]^3$ e) None of the above

Answer: _____

5.   For $f(x) = x\sqrt{x^2 - 1}$, find $f'(x)$.

Answer: _____

6. The Ivonic Heater Company has determined that the cost of producing x space heaters per day is given by $C(x) = 0.01x^2 - 0.8x + 16.5$, where $C(x)$ is measured in thousands of dollars.

A. Find the marginal cost.

   Answer: _____

B. Find $C'(40)$.

   Answer: _____

C. Find $C'(41)$.

   Answer: _____

7. If the profit, P in dollars, for a company is a function of the number of units produced, x, it can be determined that it approximates the function $P(t) = \dfrac{1000-x^2}{5-x^2}$. If the current level of production is 100 units, what is the per unit increase in profit if the production is increased from 100 to 110 units?

   Answer: _____

8. For $f(x) = \sqrt{2x}$, find $f''(x)$.

   a) $\dfrac{-1}{4\sqrt{2x}}$ b) $\dfrac{-1}{8x\sqrt{2x}}$ c) $\dfrac{-1}{4x\sqrt{2x}}$ d) $\dfrac{-1}{2x\sqrt{2x}}$ e) None of the above

   Answer: _____

9. Let $y = x^2 - \dfrac{1}{x^2}$.

A. Find $\dfrac{dy}{dx}$.

   Answer: _____

B.   Find $\dfrac{d^2y}{dx^2}$.

Answer: _____

C.   Find $\dfrac{d^3y}{dx^3}$.

Answer: _____

10. The equation of the unit circle (the circle centered at the origin of radius 1) is given by $x^2 + y^2 = 1$. Find the equation of the tangent line drawn to the point $\left(-\dfrac{\sqrt{2}}{2}, \dfrac{\sqrt{2}}{2}\right)$.

Answer: _____

11. Find $\dfrac{dy}{dx}$ by using implicit differentiation: $y^2 = 3x - 1$.

Answer: _____

12. Find $\dfrac{dy}{dx}$ if $x^2 - xy + y^2 = 4$.

Answer: _____

13. Find the slope of the tangent to the curve $x^2 - 2xy + y^2 = 1$ at $(1, 2)$.

Answer: _____

14. Find dy if $f(x) = \dfrac{2x+3}{4-x}$.

Answer: _____

15. Find dy if $f(x) = (2x-4)^2(5-x)^2$.

Answer: _____

Name_____

Section_____

1. Find the interval(s) on which $y = \frac{x}{x-4}$ is increasing and the interval(s) where it is decreasing.

   Answer: _____

2. If $f'(c) = 0$, then c is a critical point.

   a) True   b) False

   Answer: _____

3. If f has a relative maximum at $x = c$ then $f'(c) = 0$.

   a) True   b) False

   Answer: _____

4. If $f(1) = 3$, $f'(1) = 0$, and $f''(1) = 6$, then $(1, 3)$ must be:

   a) a relative minimum   b) a relative maximum   c) a point of inflection
   d) an absolute minimum   e) None of the above

   Answer: _____

5. Use the First Derivative Test to find the relative maximum and relative minimum points for the function $f(x) = x^3 - 3x$.

   Answer: _____

6. Find all asymptotes, vertical and horizontal, for the graph of $f(x) = \frac{5x^2 - 39x - 8}{x^2 - x - 12}$.

   Answer: _____

7.   If $(c, f(c))$ is a point of inflection, then $f''(c) = 0$.

      a) True   b) False

      Answer: _____

8.   Find the points of inflection for the function $g(x) = x^4 - 6x^2$.

      Answer: _____

9.   Graph $f(x) = 4x^3 - 12x^2 + 12x + 75$.

      Answer:

10.   A company has decided that the relationship between the quantity of an item sold (x) and the asking price (p) in dollars is: $p = 50 - \frac{x}{8}$, $0 \le x \le 360$.

A.   Determine the revenue equation.

      Answer: _____

B.   For what value(s) of x is revenue increasing?

      Answer: _____

C.   For what value(s) of x is revenue decreasing?

      Answer: _____

D.   What asking price will produce the maximum revenue?

      Answer: _____

E.   What is the maximum revenue?

      Answer: _____

11. A company has determined that its profit, P depends upon the amount of money spent on advertising, x. The relationship is given by the equation $P(x) = \frac{2x}{x^2+4} + 70$, where P and x are measured in thousands of dollars.

A. What amount should the company spend on advertising to assure maximum profit?

   Answer: _____

B. What is the profit?

   Answer: _____

12. Consider the relationship between profit P and selling price s (each measured in dollars): $P = 10,000s - 100s^2$.

A. Is the profit increasing or decreasing when the selling price is $40.00?

   Answer: _____

B. For what range of selling prices is profit increasing?

   Answer: _____

C. What selling price results in the maximum profit?

   Answer: _____

13. Suppose that the relationship between profit P and selling price s (each measured in dollars) is: $P = 40,000s - 200s^2$.

A. Is the profit increasing or decreasing when the selling price is $80.00?

   Answer: _____

B. For what range of selling prices is profit increasing?

   Answer: _____

C.   What selling price results in the maximum profit?

       Answer: _____

14.   Find the maximum profit when it is known that the revenue and cost functions are
       $R(x) = 500x + 70.5x^2 - x^3$ and $C(x) = 1000 + 50x$.

       Answer: _____

15.   The price of a certain stock at time t $(0 \le t \le 5)$ is estimated by
       $P(t) = 0.1t^3 + .05t^2 - 3t + 10$. When will the stock price be a maximum, and when will
       it reach a minimum?

       Answer: _____

Name_____

Section_____

1. For what values is the function $f(x) = 2x^3 - 12x^2 + 18x + 1$ increasing?

   a) all x b) $1 < x < 3$ c) $x < 1$

   d) $x < 1, x > 3$ e) Function is never increasing

   Answer: _____

2. How many critical points does $y = \sqrt{x+1} + (2x+1)^5$ have?

   a) None   b) 1   c) 2   d) 3   e) 4

   Answer: _____

3. If $f(1) = 3$, $f'(1) = 0$, and $f''(1) = 6$, then $(1, 3)$ must be:

   a) a relative minimum   b) a relative maximum   c) a point of inflection

   d) an absolute minimum   e) None of the above

   Answer: _____

4. Use the First Derivative Test to find the relative maximum and relative minimum points for the function $f(x) = x^3 - 3x$.

   Answer: _____

5. Let $f(x) = \dfrac{x}{9x^2 - 100}$.

A. Determine where $f(x)$ is concave upward.

   Answer: _____

B. Determine where $f(x)$ is concave downward.

   Answer: _____

C.   Determine any inflection points of $f(x)$.

       Answer: _____

6.   Graph $f(x) = 25x^3 - 30x^2 + 9x$ over the interval $[-1, 3]$ and identify the absolute extrema.

       Answer:

7.   Consider $f(x) = x^3 - 12x^2 - 8$. Find the points of inflection.

       a) $(0, -8)$ and $(8, -264)$ b) $(6, -224)$ c) $(4, -136)$
       d) $(0, -8)$ and $(6, 224)$ e) No points of inflection

       Answer: _____

8.   Let $y = \frac{x^2 + 1}{x}$ on the interval $[0.5, 10]$.

A.   What is the absolute minimum value of the function on the given interval?

       Answer: _____

B.   Graph the function.

       Answer:

C.   Why is there no absolute minimum value of the function on the interval $[-10, 10]$?

       Answer: _____

9.   A company has decided that the relationship between the quantity of an item sold (x) and the asking price (p) in dollars is: $p = 50 - \frac{x}{8}$, $0 \leq x \leq 360$.

A.   Determine the revenue equation.

Answer: _____

B.   For what value(s) of x is revenue increasing?

Answer: _____

C.   For what value(s) of x is revenue decreasing?

Answer: _____

D.   What asking price will produce the maximum revenue?

Answer: _____

E.   What is the maximum revenue?

Answer: _____

10.   Consider the relationship between profit P and selling price s (each measured in dollars): $P = 10,000s - 100s^2$.

A.   Is the profit increasing or decreasing when the selling price is $40.00?

Answer: _____

B.   For what range of selling prices is profit increasing?

Answer: _____

C.   What selling price results in the maximum profit?

Answer: _____

11. Suppose that the relationship between profit P and selling price s (each measured in dollars) is: $P = 40,000s - 200s^2$.

A. Is the profit increasing or decreasing when the selling price is $80.00?

Answer: _____

B. For what range of selling prices is profit increasing?

Answer: _____

C. What selling price results in the maximum profit?

Answer: _____

12. A firm has determined that its revenue $R(x)$ (measured in thousands of dollars) from the sale of x units of its product is: $R(x) = 80 - \dfrac{200}{x+4} - 2x$.

A. Find the value of x that maximizes revenue.

Answer: _____

B. Find the maximum revenue.

Answer: _____

13. Find the absolute maximum and minimum for $y = 1 - x^{\frac{5}{3}}$ on $[0, 8]$.

Answer: _____

14. Find the absolute maximum and minimum for $y = 2x^3 + 5x^2 + 4x - 6$ on $[-2, 0]$.

Answer: _____

15. What are the dimensions of the largest right circular cylinder that can be inscribed in a sphere of radius 10 in.?

Answer: _____

Name_____

Section_____

1. If $f'(c) = 0,$ then c is a critical point.

   a) True   b) False

   Answer: _____

2. If f has a relative maximum at $x = c$ then $f'(c) = 0$.

   a) True   b) False

   Answer: _____

3. Consider $y = \sqrt[3]{x}$. The point $(0,0)$ is:

   a) a relative minimum   b) a absolute minimum   c) a local maximum
   d) an absolute maximum   e) None of the above

   Answer: _____

4. Use the First Derivative Test to find the relative maximum and relative minimum points for the function $f(x) = x^4 - x^2$.

   Answer: _____

5. Let $f(x) = \dfrac{x}{9x^2 - 100}$.

A. Determine where $f(x)$ is concave upward.

   Answer: _____

B. Determine where $f(x)$ is concave downward.

   Answer: _____

C. Determine any inflection points of $f(x)$.

Answer: _____

6. Find all asymptotes, vertical and horizontal, for the graph of $f(x) = \frac{5x^2-39x-8}{x^2-x-12}$.

Answer: _____

7. Determine the symmetry, if any, and graph $f(x) = \frac{6x^2}{x^2+25}$.

Answer:

8. Graph $f(x) = \frac{8x}{x^2+7}$ and identify the absolute extrema, if any.

Answer:

9. Sketch a graph of $y = x^3 - \frac{5}{2}x^2 - 2x + \frac{1}{2}$.

Answer:

10. Graph $f(x) = 4x^3 - 12x^2 + 12x + 75$.

Answer:

11. A company has decided that the relationship between the quantity of an item sold (x) and the asking price (p) in dollars is: $p = 50 - \frac{x}{8}$, $0 \le x \le 360$.

A. Determine the revenue equation.

Answer: _____

B. For what value(s) of x is revenue increasing?

Answer: _____

C. For what value(s) of x is revenue decreasing?

Answer: _____

D. What asking price will produce the maximum revenue?

Answer: _____

229

E.   What is the maximum revenue?

     Answer: _____

12. A company has decided that the relationship between the quantity of an item sold (x)
     and the asking price (p) in dollars is: $p = 125 - \frac{x}{4}$, $0 \leq x \leq 400$.

A.   Determine the revenue equation.

     Answer: _____

B.   For what value(s) of x is revenue increasing?

     Answer: _____

C.   For what value(s) of x is revenue decreasing?

     Answer: _____

D.   What asking price will produce the maximum revenue?

     Answer: _____

E.   What is the maximum revenue?

     Answer: _____

13. Consider the relationship between profit P and selling price s (each measured in dollars):
     $P = 10,000s - 100s^2$.

A.   Is the profit increasing or decreasing when the selling price is $40.00?

     Answer: _____

B.   For what range of selling prices is profit increasing?

     Answer: _____

C.   What selling price results in the maximum profit?

Answer: _____

14.   Find the absolute maximum and minimum for $y = 2x^3 + 5x^2 + 4x - 6$ on $[-2, 0]$.

Answer: _____

15.   The price of a certain stock at time t $(0 \le t \le 5)$ is estimated by $P(t) = 0.1t^3 + 0.05t^2 - 3t + 10$. When will the stock price be a maximum, and when will it reach a minimum?

Answer: _____

1. Graph $y = e^{2x}$

   Answer:

2. Solve for x: $10^{2x-1} = 6$ (do not approximate your answer)

   Answer: _____

3. Solve for x: $e^x + 8e^{-x} - 6 = 0$

   Answer: _____

4. Find the exponential equivalent of $\log_X Y = Z$.

   a) $XY = Z$ b) $X^Z = Y$ c) $Y^X = Z$ d) $Z^X = Y$ e) None of the above

   Answer: _____

5. Solve for x: $\log_2 \dfrac{1}{\sqrt[3]{x}}$

   Answer: _____

6. The demand function for a product is described by: $p = \dfrac{300}{\ln(x+4)}$, where x represents the number of units demanded at price p.

A. Determine the price when 5 units are demanded.

   Answer: _____

B.   Determine the price when 30 units are demanded.

Answer: _____

7.   Solve for x: $\log \sqrt{x^2 + 199} = 2$.

Answer: _____

8.   Solve for x: $3 \ln 5e = 3 - \ln x$.

Answer: _____

9.   Write $10^{\frac{1}{3}} = \sqrt[3]{10}$ in logarithmic form.

Answer: _____

10.   Write $e^{-1} = \frac{1}{e}$ in logarithmic form.

Answer: _____

11.   Write $\ln x = 5$ in exponential form.

Answer: _____

12.   If $f(x) = \frac{e^{3x}}{e^{3x}+1}$, find $f'(x)$.

a) $\dfrac{3e^{3x}}{(e^{3x}+1)^2}$ b) $\dfrac{1}{(e^{3x}+1)^2}$ c) $\dfrac{e^{3x}}{e^{6x}+1}$ d) $\dfrac{3e^{6x}}{e^{6x}+1}$ e) None of the above

Answer: _____

13.   Find y' when $y = e^{x^2} + e^{x^3}$.

Answer: _____

14. If $y = \ln(4x^2 + 1)$, find $\frac{dy}{dx}$.

a) $\frac{1}{4x^2+1}$ b) $\ln 8x$ c) $\frac{8x}{4x^2+1}$ d) $\frac{1}{x}$ e) None of the above

Answer: _____

15. A certain very active bacteria grows exponentially as given by the equation $A = A_0 e^{\frac{\ln 100}{10}t}$, where A_0 is the initial bacteria count, A is the final amount, and t is the time in hours. If we begin with 600 bacteria, how many will there be after one full day?

Answer: _____

Tan Applied Calculus   Name_____
Examination 5B   Section_____

1.   Solve for x: $e^{3x+6} = 9$.

      a) $\frac{1}{3}\ln 3$ b) $\ln 3 - 2$ c) $\frac{1}{3(-6+\ln 9)}$ d) 1

      e) None of the above

      Answer: _____

2.   Simplify: $\frac{(2^{1/3})^6}{8^{2/3}}$.

      Answer: _____

3.   Graph $y = \ln(x-1) + 1$.

      Answer: _____

4.   Solve for x: $\ln \sqrt[3]{x+5} = \log_2 8$.

      Answer: _____

5.   Sociologists often assume that the rate at which a rumor spreads is based on the
      proportion of the population that has heard the rumor and the fraction of the population
      that has not. If $P(t)$ is the number of people that have heard the news, then
      $P(t) = \frac{1000P_0}{P_0 + (1000 - P_0)e^{-kt}}$, where P_0 is the number of people who have heard the
      rumor at time $t=0$ days. Find $P(1)$ if it is known that $P_0 = 10$ and $k = 5$.

      Answer: _____

6.   A secretary's typing speed (in words per minute) after t years of experience can be
      modeled by the equation $S(t) = 90 - 32\left(\frac{1}{2}\right)^t$. How long will it take to reach a typing
      speed of 80 words per minute? Give both an exact answer and an answer rounded to
      the nearest year.

      Answer: _____

7. Find the present value of $25,000 due in 5 years at an annual rate of 7 percent compounded continuously. (Round to the nearest dollar.)

Answer: _____

8. The monthly payment, P, of an amortized loan is an exponential function of the total number of payments to be made, t, and is given by the formula:
$$P = V \cdot \frac{i}{[1-(1+i)^{-t}]},$$
where V represents the amount of the loan in dollars and i represents the interest per payment period (monthly).

A. Find the monthly payment on a 15-year mortgage loan ($t = 180$) of $50,000 ($V = 50,000$) that has an annual interest rate of 12% ($i = 0.01$).

Answer: _____

B. How much interest is paid back over the life of the loan?

Answer: _____

9. Find the derivative of $f(x) = \frac{9+e^{6x}}{x}$.

Answer: _____

10. Find both the first and second derivatives of $f(x) = -5e^{2x^3}$.

Answer: _____

11. If $y = e^{x^2}$, find $\frac{dy}{dx}$.

a) $2e^{x^2}$ b) $\frac{xe^{x^2}}{2}$ c) $2xe^{x^2}$ d) $x^2e^{x^2-1}$ e) None of the above

Answer: _____

12. Find $\dfrac{d^2y}{dx^2}$ if $y = e^{x^2} + 10x$.

Answer: _____

13. If $y = \ln\left(4x^2 + 1\right)$, find $\dfrac{dy}{dx}$.

   a) $\dfrac{1}{4x^2+1}$ b) $\ln 8x$ c) $\dfrac{8x}{4x^2+1}$ d) $\dfrac{1}{x}$ e) None of the above

Answer: _____

14. Find the derivative of $y = e^{\ln x}$.

Answer: _____

15. A certain very active bacteria grows exponentially as given by the equation $A = A_0 e^{\frac{\ln 100}{10}t}$, where A_0 is the initial bacteria count, A is the final amount, and t is the time in hours. If we begin with 600 bacteria, how many will there be after one full day?

Answer: _____

Name_____

Section_____

1. Solve for x: $e^{3x+6} = 9$.

   a) $\frac{1}{3}\ln 3$ b) $\ln 3 - 2$ c) $\frac{1}{3}(-6 + \ln 9)$ d) 1 e) None of the above

   Answer: _____

2. Solve for x: $3e^{2-3x} = 19$

   Answer: _____

3. Graph $f(x) = -\left(\frac{1}{3}\right)^x$

   Answer:

4. Find the exponential equivalent of $\log_X Y = Z$.

   a) $XY = Z$ b) $X^Z = Y$ c) $Y^X = Z$ d) $Z^X = Y$ e) None of the above

   Answer: _____

5. Find the logarithmic equivalent of $X^Y = Z$.

   a) $\log_X Z = Y$ b) $Y \log X = Z$ c) $\log_X Y = Z$ d) $\log_Y Z = X$ e) None of the above

   Answer: _____

6. Solve for x: $\log_2 \dfrac{1}{\sqrt[3]{x}}$

    Answer: _____

7. Solve for x: $\log \sqrt{x^2 + 199} = 2$.

    Answer: _____

8. Write $\ln x = 5$ in exponential form.

    Answer: _____

9. A company has determined that the value V (in dollars) of its investments (which have grown at annual rate of increase of 2%) is: $V = 20,000(1.02)^t$, where t is the number of years since the investments were made. Find the value of the company's investments after five years.

    Answer: _____

10. If $f(x) = \dfrac{e^{3x}}{e^{3x}+1}$, find $f'(x)$.

    a) $\dfrac{3e^{3x}}{(e^{3x}+1)^2}$ b) $\dfrac{1}{(e^{3x}+1)^2}$ c) $\dfrac{e^{3x}}{e^{6x}+1}$ d) $\dfrac{3e^{6x}}{e^{6x}+1}$ e) None of the above

    Answer: _____

11. A company has determined that the demand for x hundred units of its product, based on the price p, is $p = 100e^{-0.05x}$.

A. Find the marginal revenue.

    Answer: _____

B. How many units should the company produce and sell to maximize its revenue?

    Answer: _____

12. Find y' when $y = x^2 e^{3x}$.

Answer: _____

13. Find y' when $y = e^{x^2} + e^{x^3}$.

Answer: _____

14. Find y' when $y = \ln e^x$.

Answer: _____

15. The graphs of which of the following exhibit exponential decay?

    a) $y = e^{-x}$ b) $y = \left(\frac{1}{2}\right)^x$ c) $y = 3^{-x}$

    d) All of the above   e) None of the above

Answer: _____

Name_____

Section_____

1. Find the function $f(x)$ such that the graph of f passes through the point $(-1,0)$ given that the slope of the tangent line to the graph at any point $(x, f(x))$ is $f'(x) = 4x^3 - 6x^2 + 6x - 3$.

   Answer: _____

2. Evaluate the following indefinite integral: $\int (\sqrt{x} + 3)^2 \left(6 + \frac{6}{x}\right) dx$.

   Answer: _____

3. The daily marginal profit associated with the production and sales of a certain product is $P'(x) = -0.000024x^2 + 6$ (in dollars per production lot), where x represents the number of production lots produced and sold each day. Each production lot consists of 10 individual units.

A. What is the total daily profit realizable if production and sale of 5000 units per day if the daily fixed cost is $200 ($P(0) = -200$)?

   Answer: _____

B. What is the additional daily profit realizable if production and sales are increased by 500 units per day?

   Answer: _____

4. Evaluate: $\int 3x^5 dx$.

   Answer: _____ .

5. Find: $\int t^{-5} dt$.

   Answer: _____

6. Find: $\int \left(x^{\frac{1}{3}} + x^{\frac{-1}{3}} \right)^2 dx.$

Answer: _____

7. Find the antiderivative of $f(x) = 4x^3 + 6x^2 - 2x + 5$, given that $f(0) = 5$.

Answer: _____

8. Find the Riemann sum approximations of the area of the region under $f(x) = 3 + \dfrac{1}{x-1}$ over the interval $[0,5]$ by partitioning the interval into two subintervals of equal length, where the points p_i, $1 \le i \le n$, of the respective subintervals are taken to be:

A. the left endpoints.

Answer: _____

B. the right endpoints.

Answer: _____

C. the midpoints.

Answer: _____

9. If the marginal cost (in dollars) for producing x units of a particular product is given by $C'(x) = 0.2x + 20$, and the fixed cost is 1500, find $C(x)$.

Answer: _____

10. Find the area bounded by the parabola $y = 6 - x - x^2$ and the x-axis.

Answer: _____

11. Evaluate: $\int\limits_{1}^{2} x\sqrt{5-x^2}\,dx$.

     a) $\dfrac{7}{2}$ b) $\dfrac{-7}{3}$ c) $\dfrac{21}{4}$ d) $\dfrac{7}{3}$ e) None of the above

     Answer: _____

12. Sketch the graphs and find the area of the region completely enclosed by the graphs of $f(x) = -x^2 + 4x$ and $g(x) = 2x - 8$.

     Answer:

13. Find the area between the two curves $y = x$ and $y = x^2 - 2x$.

     a) $\dfrac{7}{6}$ square units   b) $\dfrac{10}{3}$ square units   c) $\dfrac{9}{2}$ square units

     d) $\dfrac{1}{6}$ square units   e) None of the above

     Answer: _____

14. Find the area between the curves $f(x) = e^x$ and $g(x) = e^{-x}$ from $x = 0$ to $x = 1$.

     Answer: _____

15. If the rate of flow for an investment is $f(t) = 20,000$, find the total income produced in 7 years.

     Answer: _____

Name_____

Section_____

1. Evaluate: $\int \sqrt{x}\,(x+2)dx$.

   a) $\frac{2}{15}x^{\frac{3}{2}}(3x+10)+C$

   b) $\frac{1}{3}x^{\frac{5}{2}}(x+4)+C$

   c) $\frac{3x+2}{2\sqrt{x}}+C$

   d) $\frac{2(3x+10)}{15x\sqrt{x}}+C$

   e) None of the above

   Answer: _____

2. Evaluate: $\int \frac{2}{\sqrt{x}}dx$.

   Answer: _____

3. Evaluate: $\int \frac{2x^3+x^2+x+14}{x+2}dx$.

   Answer: _____

4. A manufacturing company has a marginal cost of $C' = 6 - 0.0004x$. If the cost of producing 100 units is $9098, find the total cost equation and the cost of producing 12,000 units.

   Answer: _____

5. Evaluate: $\int \frac{\ln x}{x}dx$.

   a) $\frac{-2}{x^3}+C$

   b) $\frac{-1}{x^2}+C$

   c) $\frac{(\ln x)^2}{2}+C$

   d) $\ln(x^2)+C$

   e) None of the above

   Answer: _____

Evaluate: $\int \frac{\ln y}{2y}dy$.

   Answer: _____

7. Evaluate: $\int t^2 (1 - t^3)^5 \, dt$.

Answer: _____

8. If the marginal cost (in dollars) for producing x units of a particular product is given by $C'(x) = 0.4x + 100$, and the fixed cost is 3500, find $C(x)$.

Answer: _____

9. What is the average value for $f(x) = x^3 + e^{\frac{x}{2}} + 6$ on $[1, 4]$?

Answer: _____

10. Find the average value for $f(x) = 4 - x^2$ between $x = -1$ to $x = 1$.

a) $\frac{22}{3}$ b) 4   c) $\frac{13}{6}$ d) $\frac{5}{3}$ e) None of the above

Answer: _____

11. Evaluate: $\int_0^1 \frac{1}{5-x} dx$.

Answer: _____

12. Find: $\int_{\sqrt{3}}^{\sqrt{8}} \frac{dx}{x\sqrt{x^2+1}}$.

Answer: _____

13. Sketch the graph and find the area of the region bounded by $f(x) = 2 - \frac{1}{3}x$, $g(x) = 5 - \frac{5}{6}x$ and the vertical line $x = 0$.

Answer:

14. If the growth rate of a city is given by the formula $P'(t) = .25e^{0.02t}$, where t is measured in years after 1985 and $P(t)$ is the population in thousands. If the population in 1987 was 35,000, predict the population (to the nearest hundred) at the turn of the century.

Answer: _____

15. Find the producer surplus given that the demand equation is $p = 500 - 10x$ and the supply equation is $p = 0.5x^2 + 100$ for a certain product, and the price is set at the equilibrium price.

Answer: _____

Tan Applied Calculus   Name_____
Examination 6C   Section_____

1. The daily marginal profit associated with the production and sales of a certain product
    is $P'(x) = -0.000024x^2 + 6$ (in dollars per production lot), where x represents the
    number of production lots produced and sold each day. Each production lot consists
    of 10 individual units.

A. What is the total daily profit realizable if production and sale of 5000 units per day if
    the daily fixed cost is $200 ($P(0) = -200$)?

    Answer: _____

B. What is the additional daily profit realizable if production and sales are increased by 500
    units per day?

    Answer: _____

2. Evaluate: $\int \left(x^4 - \frac{1}{x^3} \right) dx$

    a) $x^5 + x^4 + C$ b) $\frac{x^5}{5} - \frac{x^2}{2} + C$ c) $\frac{x^5}{5} - \frac{x^{-2}}{2} + C$

    d) $\frac{1}{10x^2}\left(2x^7 + 5\right) + C$ e) None of the above

    Answer: _____

3. Evaluate: $\int 3x^5 dx$.

    Answer: _____

4. Find: $\int x^5 dx$.

    Answer: _____

5. Find the antiderivative of $f(x) = 4x^3 + 6x^2 - 2x + 5$, given that $f(0) = 5$.

    Answer: _____

6. Evaluate: $\int (12 - 6x^2)^7 dx$.

Answer: _____

7. Find: $\int \frac{(x^2+2)}{x^3+6x} dx$.

Answer: _____

8. What is the average value of $f(x) = \frac{\ln x}{x}$ on $[1,5]$ correct to two decimal places?

Answer: _____

9. Given the definite integral $\int_0^1 \frac{x}{\sqrt{16-7x^2}} dx$, use an appropriate substitution and the properties of definite integrals to :

A. find an equivalent definite integral to be integrated and evaluated with respect to u.

Answer: _____

B. evaluate the integral.

Answer: _____

10. Evaluate: $\int_1^3 (x^2 - x + 1) dx$.

Answer: _____

11. Find the area between the two curves $y = -x^2$ and $y = x^2 - 2x$.

a) $\frac{2}{3}$ square units   b) $\frac{1}{3}$ square units   c) $\frac{5}{3}$ square units

d) 1 square units   e) None of the above

Answer: _____

12. Mr. and Mrs. Abbot are selling some property they own and have agreed to carry their own paper, subject to the following terms: The buyer is to make a down payment of $14,000 and equal monthly payments of $650 per month for 15 years. Find the present value of the purchase price of the property to the nearest dollar if the prevailing interest rate is 12 percent per annum compounded continuously.

    Answer: _____

13. Find the cost function for $C'(x) = 500 + 15.5x$ if the fixed costs are $25,000.

    Answer: _____

14. If the rate of flow for an investment is $f(t) = 100e^{0.08t}$, find the total income produced from year 5 to year 10.

    Answer: _____

15. What is the total money flow for $5000 at 5% for 5 years?

    Answer: _____

Name_____

Section_____

1.   Use a table of integrals to evaluate the following indefinite integral: $\int \left(64x^2 - 1\right)^{\frac{-3}{2}} dx.$

Answer: _____

2.   Use a table of integrals to evaluate: $\int x^3 \ln x \, dx.$

Answer: _____

3.   Find $\int xe^{5x} dx$ using an integration table.

Answer: _____

4.   Find $\int \frac{dx}{1-3e^{6x}}$ using an integration table.

Answer: _____

5.   Evaluate: $\int (3+x)e^x dx.$

Answer: _____

6.   In using the Trapezoidal Rule to approximate $\int\limits_{1}^{5} x^4 dx$ with $n = 4$, $x_0 = 1$, $x_4 = 5$, find the value for x_2.

a) 2   b) 2.2   c) 3   d) 4   e) None of the above

Answer: _____

7. Approximate (round your answer to four decimal places) the integral below using Simpson's Rule with $n = 6$.

$$\int_0^3 e^{-x^2}\, dx$$

Answer: _____

8. Approximate $\displaystyle\int_{-1}^{1} \sqrt{x^3 + 1}\, dx$ using a trapezoidal approximation where $n = 8$.

Answer: _____

9. Approximate $\displaystyle\int_{1}^{2} \frac{1}{x^2}\, dx$ using a trapezoidal approximation where $n = 2$.

Answer: _____

10. Approximate $\displaystyle\int_{-1}^{1} \sqrt{x^3 + 1}\, dx$ using Simpson's Rule where $n = 4$.

Answer: _____

11. Which of the following improper integrals converge?

a) $\displaystyle\int_{1}^{\infty} \frac{1}{x^3}\, dx$

b) $\displaystyle\int_{1}^{\infty} \frac{1}{\sqrt[3]{x}}\, dx$

c) $\displaystyle\int_{1}^{\infty} \frac{1}{\sqrt{x+4}}\, dx$

d) $\displaystyle\int_{0}^{\infty} \frac{1}{x}\, dx$

e) None of the above

Answer: _____

12. Evaluate: $\int_{-\infty}^{-1} x^{-2} dx$.

Answer: _____

13. Evaluate: $\int_{1}^{\infty} 2x^{-\frac{1}{2}} dx$.

Answer: _____

14. Evaluate: $\int_{3}^{\infty} \frac{dx}{(x+1)^3}$.

Answer: _____

15. A study has been made of the customer phone calls coming in to the switchboard of the Municipal Power Company between 8:00 AM and 12 noon on Monday mornings. The results show that the time a caller will wait on hold before being connected with a service representative is an exponentially distributed random variable x with an expected value of 44 seconds.

A. What is the probability that a customer phoning the power company on a Monday morning will have to wait on hold less than 32 seconds? (Round answer to the nearest thousandth if necessary.)

Answer: _____

B. What is the probability that a customer phoning the power company on a Monday morning will have to wait on hold more than $1\frac{1}{4}$ minutes? (Round answer to the nearest thousandth if necessary.)

Answer: _____

Tan Applied Calculus
Examination 7B

Name_____
Section_____

1. Evaluate: $\int_1^4 \ln x\, dx$.

a) $\frac{-3}{4}$ b) $\frac{3}{4}$ c) $4(\ln 4 - 1)$ d) $4\ln 4 - 3$ e) None of the above

Answer: _____

2. Use a table of integrals to evaluate: $\int x^3 \ln x\, dx$.

Answer: _____

3. Find $\int \frac{dx}{\sqrt{x^2-2}}$ using an integration table.

Answer: _____

4. Find $\int xe^{5x}\, dx$ using an integration table.

Answer: _____

5. Find $\int \frac{dx}{1-3e^{6x}}$ using an integration table.

Answer: _____

6. In using the Trapezoidal Rule to approximate $\int_2^5 x^4\, dx$ with $n = 4$, $x_0 = 2$, $x_4 = 5$, find the value for x_3.

a) 3.5   b) 4.67   c) 3   d) 2.75   e) None of the above

Answer: _____

7. Approximate $\int_0^1 x^3 dx$ using a trapezoidal approximation where $n = 2$.

Answer: _____

8. Evaluate the following improper integral if it is convergent: $\int_2^\infty 4(2x+1)^{-2} dx$.

Answer: _____

9. Find the area of the region under $f(x) = 7e^{-4x}$ over the interval $[0, \infty)$.

Answer: _____

10. Which of the following improper integrals converge?

a) $\int_1^\infty \frac{1}{x^3} dx$

b) $\int_1^\infty \frac{1}{\sqrt[3]{x}} dx$

c) $\int_1^\infty \frac{1}{\sqrt{x+4}} dx$

d) $\int_0^\infty \frac{1}{x} dx$

e) None of the above

Answer: _____

11. Find the area between the two curves $y = e^{-x}$ and $y = -e^{-x}$ for $x \geq 0$.

Answer: _____

12. Evaluate: $\int_0^\infty 100e^{-0.1x} dx$.

Answer: _____

13. Evaluate: $\displaystyle\int_{-\infty}^{-1} x^{-2}\,dx$.

Answer: _____

14. Evaluate: $\displaystyle\int_{3}^{\infty} \frac{dx}{(x+1)^3}$.

Answer: _____

15. Determine the value of the constant k such that $f(x) = \dfrac{k}{\sqrt{x-8}}$ is a probability density function on the interval $[8, 24]$.

Answer: _____

1. Use integration by parts to evaluate the following indefinite integral: $\int (8x - 7)e^x dx$.

    Answer: _____

2. Evaluate: $\int \ln \sqrt{x}\, dx$.

    a) $\frac{x}{2} \ln x - \frac{x}{2} + C$ b) $\frac{x}{2} + C$ c) $x \ln \sqrt{x} - \frac{2}{3}\sqrt{x^3} + C$

    d) $x \ln \sqrt{x} - \frac{1}{\sqrt{x}} + C$ e) None of the above

    Answer: _____

3. Evaluate: $\int_{1}^{3} \ln x\, dx$.

    a) $\frac{-2}{3}$ b) $\frac{2}{3}$ c) $3(\ln 3 - 1)$ d) $3\ln 3 - 2$ e) None of the above

    Answer: _____

4. Find $\int xe^{5x} dx$ using an integration table.

    Answer: _____

5. Approximate (round your answer to four decimal places) the integral below using Simpson's Rule with $n = 6$.

    $$\int_{0}^{3} e^{-x^2} dx$$

    Answer: _____

6. Estimate the area of an ellipse centered at the origin with major axis of 6 along the x-axis, given the following first quadrant points on the ellipse: $(0.5, 1.98), (1.0, 1.89),$ $(1.5, 1.73), (2.0, 1.49), (2.5, 1.11), (3.0, 0)$.

   Answer: _____

7. Approximate $\int_{-1}^{1} \sqrt{x^3 + 1}\, dx$ using a trapezoidal approximation where $n = 8$.

   Answer: _____

8. Approximate $\int_{1}^{2} \frac{1}{x^2}\, dx$ using a trapezoidal approximation where $n = 2$.

   Answer: _____

9. Find the area of the region under $f(x) = 7e^{-4x}$ over the interval $[0, \infty)$.

   Answer: _____

10. Which of the following improper integrals converge?

    a) $\int_{1}^{\infty} \frac{1}{x^3}\, dx$

    b) $\int_{1}^{\infty} \frac{1}{\sqrt[3]{x}}\, dx$

    c) $\int_{1}^{\infty} \frac{1}{\sqrt{x+4}}\, dx$

    d) $\int_{1}^{\infty} \frac{1}{x}\, dx$

    e) None of the above

    Answer: _____

11. Evaluate: $\int_{-\infty}^{-2} \frac{2}{(x+1)^2}\, dx$.

    a) 2   b) –2   c) $\frac{2}{3}$ d) 0   e) None of the above

    Answer: _____

12. Find the area between the two curves $y = e^{-x}$ and $y = -e^{-x}$ for $x \geq 0$.

Answer: _____

13. Evaluate: $\displaystyle\int_{-\infty}^{-1} x^{-2}\,dx$.

Answer: _____

14. Evaluate: $\displaystyle\int_{1}^{\infty} 2x^{-\frac{1}{2}}\,dx$.

Answer: _____

15. A study has been made of the customer phone calls coming in to the switchboard of the Municipal Power Company between 8:00 AM and 12 noon on Monday mornings. The results show that the time a caller will wait on hold before being connected with a service representative is an exponentially distributed random variable x with an expected value of 44 seconds.

A. What is the probability that a customer phoning the power company on a Monday morning will have to wait on hold less than 32 seconds? (Round answer to the nearest thousandth if necessary.)

Answer: _____

B. What is the probability that a customer phoning the power company on a Monday morning will have to wait on hold more than $1\frac{1}{4}$ minutes? (Round answer to the nearest thousandth if necessary.)

Answer: _____

Name_____

Section_____

1. Suppose that $f(x,y) = 3x^2 - 4x^2y - 2y^2$. Find $\frac{\partial f}{\partial x}$.

    a) $6x - 8xy$ b) $6x - 8xy - 4y$ c) $6x - 4x^2 + 8xy - 4y$

    d) $-2x$ e) None of the above

    Answer: _____

2. If $z = F(x,y) = \dfrac{50}{x^2+y^2}$, find $\dfrac{\partial z}{\partial x}$.

    Answer: _____

3. Let $f(x,y) = 2y^3 - x^2 + 12y^2 + 4x - 30y + 15$.

A. Find the critical points, if any.

    Answer: _____

B. State the results of applying the Second Derivative Test at each critical point, naming any relative extema.

    Answer: _____

4. Let $f(x,y) = \dfrac{2x - 5y^3}{xy^3}$.

A. Find the critical points, if any.

    Answer: _____

B. State the results of applying the Second Derivative Test at each critical point, naming any relative extema.

    Answer: _____

5. Find the relative extrema and saddle points for $f(x,y) = 2x^3 - 6xy + y^3$.

Answer: _____

6. Evaluate: $\displaystyle\int_1^5 \int_{(y-3)^2+1}^5 6\,dx\,dy$.

Answer: _____

7. Evaluate: $\displaystyle\int_0^1 \int_{e^x}^e \frac{1}{\ln y}\,dy\,dx$ by reversing the order of integration.

Answer: _____

8. A furniture company has found that the labor cost, L, for the production of its finished furniture pieces is the foolowing function of construction time, c, and finishing time, f:
$L(c,f) = c^2 + 6cf + 10f^2 - 16c - 52f + 110$. Find the minimum labor cost and the number of hours of construction and finishing required.

Answer: _____

9. Find the line of best fit for the following data points.

x	y
0	4
-2	0
1	5

a) $y = \frac{12}{7}x + \frac{25}{7}$ 　　　b) $y = 2x + 3$ 　　　c) $y = \frac{25}{7}x + \frac{12}{7}$

d) $y = \frac{12}{7}x - \frac{25}{7}$ 　　　e) None of the above

Answer: _____

10. Find the line of best fit for the following data points.

x	y
0	10
–2	4
2	12

a) $y = \frac{26}{3}x + 2$ b) $y = 2x + 8$ c) $y = 2x - \frac{26}{3}$

d) $y = 2x + \frac{26}{3}$ e) None of the above

Answer: _____

11. An entrance examination into a certain mathematics class is administered. At the end of the semester, the class grade is compared with their class standing, as shown on the following table:

Class Standing:	1	2	3	4	5	6	7	8	9	10
Entrance examination	85	80	90	70	80	50	60	65	50	45

Find the regression line.

Answer: _____

12. A study of the number of coronary attacks per 100 individuals, in various income groups gave the following data (income in thousands of dollars):

Income:	0-10	10-20	20-30	30-40	40-50	50-60	60-70	70-80	80-90	90-100
Attacks:	57	59	61	56	53	55	59	61	65	71

Find the regression line.

Answer: _____

13. At Frost Machine Tools, x units of labor and y units of capital are necessary to complete $f(x,y) = 110x^{3/4}y^{1/4}$ units of their product. The unit costs of labor and capital are $100 and $250, respectively, with a total of $120,000 allocated for production next quarter. Using the Method of Lagrange Multipliers, determine the number of units of labor and the number of units of capital that must be utilized in order to maximize quarterly production.

Answer: _____

14. Evaluate the double integral for $f(x,y) = -6y$, where R is bounded by $y = \frac{2}{3}x$ and $y = \sqrt{4x}$.

Answer: _____

15. Evaluate the double integral for $f(x,y) = (y-1)^{-1/2}e^{2y}$, where R is bounded by the y-axis $x = 0$, the horizontal line $y = 5$, and $y = x^2 + 1$.

Answer: _____

1. If $V(a, b, h) = \pi abh$, find $V(5, 7, 12)$.

    Answer: _____

2. Compute the first partial derivatives of $f(x, y) = x^4 - 4y^3 + 2xy$.

    Answer: _____

3. Suppose that $f(x, y) = 5x^2 - 4x^2 y - 2y^2$. Find $\frac{\partial f}{\partial x}$.

    a) $10x - 8xy$ b) $10x - 8xy - 4y$ c) $10x - 4x^2 + 8xy - 4y$
    d) $2x$ e) None of the above

    Answer: _____

4. If $f(x, y) = e^{x^2 + y^2}$, find f_x .

    Answer: _____

5. If $z = F(x, y) = \frac{5xy}{x+y}$, find $\frac{\partial z}{\partial x}$.

    Answer: _____

6. If $z = F(x, y) = \frac{5xy}{x+y}$, find $\frac{\partial^2 z}{\partial x^2}$.

    Answer: _____

7. Find two numbers whose product is a maximum subject to $x + y = 8$.

    Answer: _____

8. Evaluate: $\int_{-3}^{1} (x^2 + 2xy + y^3)\,dy$.

Answer: _____

9. Reggie Construction estimates that the profit (in thousands of dollars) made on the construction of several buildings is $P(x,y) = -5 + 10x - x^2 + 6y - y^2$, where x is the number of projects in Miami and y is the number of construction projects in Tampa. How many construction projects in each city will yield the maximum profit?

Answer: _____

10. A furniture company has found that the labor cost, L, for the production of its finished furniture pieces is the following function of construction time, c, and finishing time, f: $L(c,f) = c^2 + 6cf + 10f^2 - 16c - 52f + 110$. Find the minimum labor cost and the number of hours of construction and finishing required.

Answer: _____

11. Compare IQ with achievement level in a certain English class

IQ	105	87	110	101	85	90
Class score	85	110	80	90	100	110

Find the regression line.

Answer: _____

12. At Frost Machine Tools, x units of labor and y units of capital are necessary to complete $f(x,y) = 110x^{3/4}y^{1/4}$ units of their product. The unit costs of labor and capital are \$100 and \$250, respectively, with a total of \$120,000 allocated for production next quarter. Using the Method of Lagrange Multipliers, determine the number of units of labor and the number of units of capital that must be utilized in order to maximize quarterly production.

Answer: _____

13. Evaluate the double integral for $f(x,y) = -6y$, where R is bounded by $y = \frac{2}{3}x$ and $y = \sqrt{4x}$.

Answer: _____

14. The population density of a certain college town is given by the function $f(x,y) = 9000e^{-0.2|x|-0.3|y|}$ where x and y are in miles and the origin gives the location of the center of the college campus. What is the population inside the rectangular area described by $D = \{(x,y)| \; 0 \leq x \leq 4, \; -7 \leq y \leq 7\}$, to the nearest whole number?

Answer: _____

15. Find the average value of $f(x,y) = x$ over the triangular plane region bounded by $y = 8 - 4x$, and the y-axis.

Answer: _____

Tan Applied Calculus
Examination 8C

Name_____

Section_____

1.   If $g(x,y) = \ln(x^2 + y^2)$, find $g(3,9)$ to four decimal places.

       Answer: _____

2.   If $A(P,i,n) = P(1+i)^n$, find $A(5500, 0.12, 10)$ to the nearest hundredth.

       Answer: _____

3.   If $V(l,w,h) = lwh$, find $V(25, 8, 4)$.

       Answer: _____

4.   Compute the first partial derivatives of $f(x,y) = x^2 \ln(x^2 + y^3)$.

       Answer: _____

5.   If $f(x,y) = 3x^3 + 6y^2 - 4x^2y^2$, find $f_{xx}(1,2)$.

       a) 14   b) –2   c) 6   d) –14   e) None of the above

       Answer: _____

7.   Let $f(x,y) = 2y^3 - x^2 + 12y^2 + 4x - 30y + 15$.

A.   Find the critical points, if any.

       Answer: _____

B.   State the results of applying the Second Derivative Test at each critical point, naming any relative extema.

       Answer: _____

8.	Consider the function $f(x,y) = 3x^2 + 3y^2 + 4xy - 8x + 4y + 2$. Find the critical points and then determine any relative maxima, relative minima, or saddle points for the function.

	Answer: _____

9.	Find the relative maximum of $f(x,y) = 4 - x + 2y$ subject to $x^2 = y^2 = 9$.

	Answer: _____

10.	Evaluate: $\displaystyle\int_0^4 \int_0^{\sqrt{y}} 3xy \, dy \, dx$ by reversing the order of integration.

	Answer: _____

11.	Evaluate: $\displaystyle\int_0^1 \int_{e^x}^{e} \frac{1}{\ln y} \, dy \, dx$ by reversing the order of integration.

	Answer: _____

12.	Find the volume of the region defined by: $\displaystyle\iint_R x^2 y \, dy \, dx \begin{cases} 0 \le x \le 3 \\ 2 \le y \le 4 \end{cases}$.

	Answer: _____

13.	Find the volume of the region defined by: $\displaystyle\iint_R (x^2 + xy - y^2) \, dA$ bounded by $y = x$ and $y = x^2$.

	Answer: _____

14. Consider the following data:

x	y
2	5
4	10
6	12

Find the line of best fit.

Answer: _____

15. Consider the following data:

x	y
−2	−1
−1	1
0	2
1	3
2	5

Find the line of best fit.

Answer: _____

1. Find the general solution for $\frac{dy}{dx} = y^2(2x-1)$.

a) $-\frac{1}{y} = x^2 - x + C$

b) $-\frac{y^3}{3} = x^2 - x + C$

c) $-\frac{2}{y^3} = x^2 + C$

d) $y = \frac{y^3}{3}(x^2 - x) + C$

e) None of the above

Answer: _____

2. Find the general solution for $\frac{dy}{dx} = \frac{2y}{x^2}$.

a) $\ln|y| = -\frac{4}{x^3} + C$

b) $-\frac{1}{y^2} = -\frac{4}{x^3} + C$

c) $-\frac{1}{y^2} = -\frac{2}{x}C$

d) $\ln|y| = -\frac{2}{x} + C$

e) None of the above

Answer: _____

3. Find the general solution for $4x - y^2\frac{dy}{dx} + 1 = 0$.

Answer: _____

4. Find the general solution for the following differential equation: $5y^2 + xyy' = -45$.

Answer: $x^{10}(y^2 + 9) = C$

5. Given $x^3 y\frac{dy}{dx} + y^2 = 0$, find the particular solution given that the curve passes through the point $(-1, 1)$.

a) $\frac{x^4 y^2}{8} + \frac{y^3}{3} - \frac{11}{24} = 0$

b) $-\frac{y^2}{2} = \frac{x^4}{4} - \frac{3}{4}$

c) $\ln|y| = \frac{1}{2x^2} - \frac{1}{2}$

d) $\ln|y| = \frac{1}{3x^2} - \frac{1}{3}$

e) None of the above

Answer: _____

6. The rate at which a new employee can produce units on an assembly line is proportional to the difference between the maximum number of units (80) and the number of units (x) produced per day. Find a differential equation describing this relationship.

a) $\frac{dx}{dt} = k(x - 80)$ b) $\frac{dx}{dt} = k(80 - x)$ c) $\frac{dx}{dt} = x(80 - x)$

d) $\frac{dx}{dt} = 80 - kx$ e) None of the above

Answer: _____

7. Find the equation of f given that: (1) the slope of the tangent line to the graph of f at any point $P(x,y)$ is given by the expression $\frac{dy}{dx} = -5x^3$; and (2) the graph of f passes through the point $\left(1, \frac{1}{12}\right)$.

Answer: _____

8. A certain fungus has been found to thrive on the filters of the climate-control system in a certain building when a constant temperature of $70^{o}F$ is maintained within the building, with the growth rate of the fungus on a filter proportional to the number of fungi on that filter at any time t. If there were 800 fungi present initially on a sample filter from the building and 1500 fungi present 3 days later, how many fungi will be on the filter at the end of 12 days if the ideal temperature is maintained?

Answer: _____

9. A tank initially contains 10 gallons of pure water. Brine containing 4 pounds of salt per gallon flows into the tank at a rate of 3 gallons per minute and the well-stirred mixture flows out of the tank at the same rate. Find the amount of salt present in the tank:

A.   at any time t.

Answer: _____

B.   at the end of 25 minutes.

Answer: _____

C.   in the long run.

Answer: _____

10. Suppose that $2000 is deposited into an account. The account balance increases as it earns interest at 9% per year, compounded continuously. Find a differential equation describing this rate of change if A represents the amount of money in the account at any time t.

a) $\frac{dA}{dt} = 2000 + 0.09A$ b) $\frac{dA}{dt} = 90A$ c) $\frac{dA}{dt} = 0.09A$

d) $\frac{dA}{dt} = e^{0.09t}$ e) None of the above

Answer: _____

11. Solve $\frac{dy}{dx} = x^2 y^{-1}$ for y if $y = 8$ when $x = 3$.

Answer: _____

12. Solve $\frac{dy}{dx} = \frac{x^2 y^3}{y^2 - 2y + 3}$ for y if $y = 1$ when $x = 0$.

Answer: _____

13. Find $\int (5 - 3x)(2x - 1)^4 dx$ by using parts.

Answer: _____

14. If inflation over the past five years has averaged 4.5%, how long will it take (to the nearest year) for $100 to be worth what $10 is worth today?

Answer: _____

15. A certain bacterial culture is growing at a rate proportional to the amount present. If the culture began with 500 bacteria and 5 hours later had grown to 1600, how many will there be in 24 hours?

Answer: _____

271

Name_____

Section_____

1. You are given the differential equation: $y' - 8x^3 y = 0$.

A. Show that $y = Ce^{2x^4}$ is a general solution of the differential equation.

Answer: _____

B. Find a particular solution to the differential equation satisfying the side condition: $y(1) = \frac{1}{3}$.

Answer: _____

2. Find the general solution for the following differential equation: $y' = \dfrac{6xy^4}{e^{x^2}(y^8 - 1)}$.

Answer: _____

3. Find the general solution for the following differential equation: $5y^2 + xyy' = -45$.

Answer: _____

4. The rate at which a new employee can produce units on an assembly line is proportional to the difference between the maximum number of units (80) and the number of units (x) produced per day. Find a differential equation describing this relationship.

   a) $\frac{dx}{dt} = k(x - 80)$ b) $\frac{dx}{dt} = k(80 - x)$ c) $\frac{dx}{dt} = x(80 - x)$

   d) $\frac{dx}{dt} = 80 - kx$ e) None of the above

Answer: _____

5. Find the equation of f given that: (1) the slope of the tangent line to the graph of f at any point $P(x, y)$ is given by the expression $\frac{dy}{dx} = -5x^3$; and (2) the graph of f passes through the point $\left(1, \frac{1}{12}\right)$.

   Answer: _____

6. A tank initially contains 10 gallons of pure water. Brine containing 4 pounds of salt per gallon flows into the tank at a rate of 3 gallons per minute and the well-stirred mixture flows out of the tank at the same rate. Find the amount of salt present in the tank:

A. at any time t.

   Answer: _____

B. at the end of 25 minutes.

   Answer: _____

C. in the long run.

   Answer: _____

7. Use Euler's Method with $n = 5$ to obtain an approximation of the initial value problem $y' = x - y + 1$, $y(0) = 1$ when $x = 0.5$. (Round answer to the nearest ten-thousandth if necessary.)

   Answer: _____

8. Solve: $3yy' = x - 3$.

   Answer: _____

9. Solve: $y' = x^2 \sqrt{y}$.

   Answer: _____

10. Solve $y^2 y' = e^{x+3}$ for y if $y = e$ when $x = 1$.

    Answer: _____

11. Find $\int xe^{4x}\,dx$ by using parts.

    Answer: _____

12. Find $\int (5x+3)e^{-4x}\,dx$ by using parts.

    Answer: _____

13. If inflation over the past five years has averaged 4.5%, how long will it take (to the nearest year) for $100 to be worth what $10 is worth today?

    Answer: _____

14. Newton's Law of Cooling states that the temperature T of a cooling object drops at a rate which is proportional to the difference $T - M$, where M is the constant temperature of the surrounding medium. Thus, $\frac{dT}{dt} = -k(T - M)$, where k is a positive constant depending on the object which is cooling. Solve this differential equation.

    Answer: _____

15. A certain bacterial culture is growing at a rate proportional to the amount present. If the culture began with 500 bacteria and 5 hours later had grown to 1600, how many will there be in 24 hours?

    Answer: _____

1. Find the general solution for $\dfrac{dy}{dx} = y^2(2x-1)$.

    a) $-\dfrac{1}{y} = x^2 - x + C$ b) $-\dfrac{y^3}{3} = x^2 - x + C$ c) $-\dfrac{2}{y^3} = x^2 + C$

    d) $y = \dfrac{y^3}{3}(x^2 - x) + C$ e) None of the above

    Answer: _____

2. You are given the differential equation: $y' - 8x^3 y = 0$.

A. Show that $y = Ce^{2x^4}$ is a general solution of the differential equation.

    Answer: _____

B. Find a particular solution to the differential equation satisfying the side condition: $y(1) = \dfrac{1}{3}$.

    Answer: _____

3. Given $2x^2 y\dfrac{dy}{dx} + x^3 = 0$, find the particular solution given that the curve passes through the point $(-2, 2)$.

    a) $x^2 + 2y^2 = 12$ b) $y^2 = -\dfrac{x^2}{2} + 4$ c) $y^2 = -\dfrac{x^2}{2} + 2$
    d) $2y^2 = 6 - x^2$ e) None of the above

    Answer: _____

4.   The rate at which a new employee can produce units on an assembly line is proportional to the difference between the maximum number of units (80) and the number of units (x) produced per day. Find a differential equation describing this relationship.

a) $\dfrac{dx}{dt} = k(x - 80)$ b) $\dfrac{dx}{dt} = k(80 - x)$ c) $\dfrac{dx}{dt} = x(80 - x)$

d) $\dfrac{dx}{dt} = 80 - kx$ e) None of the above

Answer: _____

5.   By the time the local health department declared an outbreak of the Balinese flu to have reached the epidemic level, 4 percent of the 1000 children attending Enchantment Valley Elementary School had already contracted the virus. The rate at which the flu spreads is jointly proportional to the number of students who have the flu and the number of students who have not yet contracted the disease. If, in the next ten days, 14 percent of the children had contracted the flu, how many of the students had contracted the virus after another ten days?

Answer: _____

6.   A tank initially contains 10 gallons of pure water. Brine containing 4 pounds of salt per gallon flows into the tank at a rate of 3 gallons per minute and the well-stirred mixture flows out of the tank at the same rate. Find the amount of salt present in the tank:

A.   at any time t.

Answer: _____

B.   at the end of 25 minutes.

Answer: _____

C.   in the long run.

Answer: _____

7. Use Euler's Method with $n = 5$ to obtain an approximation of the initial value problem $y' = x - y + 1$, $y(0) = 1$ when $x = 0.5$. (Round answer to the nearest ten-thousandth if necessary.)

Answer: _____

8. Solve: $\dfrac{dy}{dx} = 2xy + y$.

Answer: _____

9. Solve: $3yy' = x - 3$.

Answer: _____

11. Solve $y' = 3x^2 - 4x + 5$ for y if $y = 3$ when $x = 0$.

Answer: _____

12. Solve $\dfrac{dy}{dx} = \dfrac{x^2 y^3}{y^2 - 2y + 3}$ for y if $y = 1$ when $x = 0$.

Answer: _____

13. Solve $y^2 y' = e^{x+3}$ for y if $y = 3$ when $x = 0$.

Answer: _____

14. Find $\int xe^{4x}\,dx$ by using parts.

Answer: _____

15. Find $\int (\ln x)(x^2 + 4x - 5)\,dx$ by using parts.

Answer: _____

Tan Applied Calculus
Examination 10

Name_____

Section_____

1. Find the fourth Taylor polynomial of $f(x) = \frac{1}{x-2}$ at $x = 0$.

   Answer: _____

2. Use four iterations of Newton's method on an appropriate function $f(x)$ and initial guess $x_0 = 6$ to obtain an estimate of $\sqrt{26}$. (Round the answer to four decimal places.)

   Answer: _____

3. You are given the sequence: 1, 8, 27, 64,... .

A. Find the general term.

   Answer: _____

B. Discuss the convergence. If the sequence converges, find its limits.

   Answer: _____

4. Express the repeating decimal 1.57575757... as a rational number.

   Answer: _____

5. Find the radius of convergence and the interval of convergence for the power series:
   $$\sum_{n=0}^{\infty} \frac{(x+2)^n}{2^n}.$$

   Answer: _____

6. Given the Taylor series, $\frac{1}{1-x} = 1 + x + x^2 + ... + x^n + ..., -1 \leq x \leq 1$, find the Taylor series and the interval of convergence for $f(x) = \frac{1}{2x-9}$ at $x = 0$.

   Answer: _____

7. Given the Taylor series, $\ln(1+x) = x - \frac{1}{2}x^2 + \frac{1}{3}x^3 - \ldots + \frac{(-1)^{n+1}}{n}x^n + \ldots$, differentiate to find the Taylor series for $f(x) = \frac{1}{36x^2+1}$ at $x = 0$.

Answer: _____

8. Use a fourth-degree Taylor polynomial to approximate $\int_0^{0.3} \left(1+x^2\right)^{-\frac{1}{5}} dx$ to the nearest ten-thousandth.

Answer: _____

Tan Applied Calculus
Examination 11

Name_____

Section_____

1.   Convert -405° to radian measure.

     Answer: _____

2.   Convert $\frac{10}{3}\pi$ radians to degree measure.

     Answer: _____

3.   Evaluate: $\cos\frac{\pi}{4}$.

     Answer: $\frac{\sqrt{2}}{2}$

4.   Find all values of θ that satisfy the equation: $\cos\theta = \frac{1}{2}$ over the interval $[0, 2\pi]$.

     Answer: _____

5.   Sketch the graph of : $y = -2\cos 3x$.

     Answer:

6.   Find the derivative of the function: $f(x) = \sec^2 x \sin x$.

     Answer: _____

280

7.   Find the equation of the tangent line to the graph of the function: $f(x) = \sec x$ at the point $\left(\frac{\pi}{4}, \sqrt{2}\right)$.

Answer: _____

8.   The height of a pier over the water level on a particular day is given by $h = 28 + 8\cos\frac{4\pi(t-5)}{23}$ feet, where $t = 0$ corresponds to 12 midnight. Determine the times of high and low tide for that day.

Answer: _____

9.   Evaluate the integral: $\int \sec^2 x \sin x \, dx$.

Answer: _____

10. The number of bees on a beehive during the month of April is given by the expression $N = 10,000 - 9000\cos\frac{2\pi(t-1)}{64}$, where t is in days and $t = 1$ corresponds to April 1st. Determine the average number of bees on the beehive for the week between the 9th and 16th of April.

Answer: _____

Answers to
Chapter Tests

Tan Applied Calculus
Examination 1A-Answer Key

1. $\dfrac{1}{8}$

2. $(-\infty, -(\pi + \sqrt{7}))$

3. $\dfrac{2}{3}, -4$

4. $x^3 - 4x^2 + x + 6$

5. $\dfrac{4}{9}$

6. $\dfrac{\pm 2\sqrt{6}}{3}$

7. A) $9x^2 + 12x + 4$

   B) $9x^2 + 6x + 1$

8. A) $2x^2 - 9xy + 4y^2$

   B) $2x^2 + 5xy - 12y^2$

9. A) $15x^2 - 11x - 60$

   B) $6x^4 - 11x^2 y - 10y^2$

10. $(7x - 13)(13x - 11)$

11. $x + y - 5 = 0$

12. $(2, -3)$

13. $\dfrac{39}{35}$

14. $6x + y - 1150 = 0$

15. 92.20

Examination 1B-Answer Key

1. $\dfrac{\sqrt{x}}{2}$

2. $\left(\dfrac{11}{3}, \infty\right)$

3. $\left[\dfrac{11}{2}, \dfrac{17}{2}\right]$

4. $\dfrac{x}{x + \sqrt{x}}$

5. $\dfrac{4(2x^2 + 1)}{\sqrt{x^2 + 1}}$

6. $\dfrac{4}{9}$

7. $\dfrac{-1 \pm \sqrt{3}}{2}$

8. A) $9x^2 + 12x + 4$

   B) $9x^2 + 6x + 1$

9. A) $15x^2 - 11x - 60$

   B) $6x^4 - 11x^2 y - 10y^2$

10. $(3 + x)(2 - 3x)$

11. $\dfrac{-39}{24}$

12. $10, \dfrac{5}{2}$

13. $\dfrac{-1}{4}$

14. -1

15. $6x + y - 1150 = 0$

1. $\dfrac{1}{4}$

2. $[-16, -2]$

3. $[0, 1]$

4. $-3, 6$

5. $(2-x)(2+x)\left(x^2+4\right)$

6. A) $x^2 + 2x - 15$

   B) $2x^2 - 13x + 20$

7. A) $9x^2 + 12x + 4$

   B) $9x^2 + 6x + 1$

8. A) $2x^2 - 9xy + 4y^2$

   B) $2x^2 + 5xy - 12y^2$

9. $184.50

10. $4x + y - 12 = 0$

11. $\left(0, \dfrac{4}{3}\right)$

12. $\dfrac{400}{3}, 40$

13. $4, 3$

14. $\dfrac{-1}{4}$

15. $10x + 6y = 7$

1.

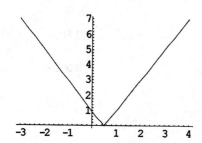

2.   23

3.   8

4.   −1

5.   1000

6.   continuous

7.   1

8.   9

9. $\frac{5}{2}x^{\frac{-1}{2}}$

10. −24

11. A)   48 feet per second

B)   48 feet per second

12. A) $y = -2x + 2$

B)

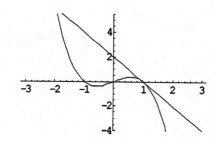

13. 2

14. A) $-4x - 2h$

B) $-4x$

15. $\frac{2}{5}$

1. $x \geq -2$

2. 12

3. $4200

4. A) $p = \frac{1}{30}x + 50$ B) $(3000, 150)$

5. $\frac{-5}{3}$

6. $\frac{1}{8}$

7. 1

8. $x = -\sqrt{2}$

9. A)   7.8   B)   6

10. $\frac{-5}{6}$

11. $\frac{-5}{2}$

12. $3x^2$

13. $\frac{5}{2}x^{\frac{-1}{2}}$

14. A) $y = -2x + 2$

    B)

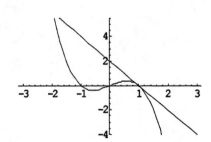

15. A) $-2x - h$ B) $-2x$

Tan Applied Calculus
Examination 2C-Answer Key

1. −21

2. 12

3. $1800

4. −3

5. 3

6. Limit does not exist

7. 2000

8. Discontinuous at $x = 2$

9. $3x^2$

10 A) 0.01   B)   0

11. A)   −96 feet per second   B) −96 feet per second

12. $2x − 8$

13. A) $−2x − h$ B) $−2x$

14. A) $0.04x + 40$ B) $40.80 per chair

15. i) and ii)

1. $50x^{-3}$

2. $\frac{-8}{3}x^3 + 3\sqrt{2}\,x^2 - 23$

3. $-\frac{1}{x^3} - \frac{6}{x^4}$

4. $6(3x+2)(3x^2+4x-1)^2$

5. $-2(2-5x)(3x^2+1)^3(75x^2-24x+5)$

6. $y' = -12x^3$; $y'' = -36x^2$; $y''' = -72x$; $y^{(iv)} = -72$; all of the rest are zero.

7. $f''(0) = -8$; $f''\left(\frac{8}{15}\right) = 8$

8. A) $\dfrac{-1}{x\sqrt{x}}$

   B) $\dfrac{3}{2x^2\sqrt{x}}$

   C) $\dfrac{-15}{4x^3\sqrt{x}}$

9. $\frac{2-x}{y}$

10. $\frac{1}{10}\pi$ ft/sec

11. $-\frac{x}{y}$

12. $\frac{2x-y}{x-2y}$

13. 1

14. $\frac{193}{487} \approx 4.0208333$

15. 0.000018

Tan Applied Calculus
Examination 3B-Answer Key

1. A) $P'(t) = 6t^2 + 6t - 2$

    B)   118,000 per year

2. $x - y = 0$

3. $\dfrac{-4}{25}$

4. -0.0463

5. $6x^3\left(6x^2 - 15x + 20\right)$

6. $\dfrac{2}{x^3}$

7. $-2(2 - 5x)\left(3x^2 + 1\right)^3\left(75x^2 - 24x + 5\right)$

8. A) $110x - 0.2x^2$

    B) $110x - 0.2x^2 - 1200$

    C) $110x - 0.4x$

9. 0.019919915; the per unit increase in profit is about \$.02

10. $y' = -\frac{1}{2}x^{-2} + x^{-3}$; $y'' = x^{-3} - 3x^{-4}$; $y''' = -3x^{-4} + 12x^{-5}$; $y^{(iv)} = 12x^{-5} - 60x^{-6}$

11. $y = x + \sqrt{2}$

12. $\dfrac{3(3x+4)}{2(2y+4)}$

13. $\dfrac{5}{3}$

14. A)   0.61   B)   0.6

15. $\Delta y \approx 0.003444$; $dy \approx 0.003472$

1.   A) $P'(t) = 6t^2 + 6t - 2$ B)   118,000 per year

2. $\dfrac{2 - 6t - 2t^2}{(t^2 + 1)^2}$

3. $-10x + 28$

4. $-8[g(x)]^3 \cdot g'(x)$

5. $(x^2 - 1)^{\frac{-1}{2}}(2x^2 - 1)$

6   A) $C'(x) = 0.02x - 0.8$ B)   0

       C)   \$20 per heater

7.   0.019919915; the per unit increase in profit is about \$.02

8. $\dfrac{-1}{2x\sqrt{2x}}$

9.   A) $2x + \dfrac{2}{x^3}$ B) $2 - \dfrac{6}{x^4}$

       C) $\dfrac{24}{x^5}$

10. $y = x + \sqrt{2}$

11. $\dfrac{3}{2y}$

12. $\dfrac{2x - y}{x - 2y}$

13.   1

14. $11(4 - x)^{-2}dx$

15. $4(x - 2)(5 - x)^2(16 - 5x)dx$

1.   Decreasing: $(-\infty, 4) \cup (4, \infty)$; never increasing

2.   True

3.   False

4.   a local minimum

5. $(1, -2)$ is a relative minimum; $(-1, 2)$ is a relative maximum

6.   Horizontal asymptote: $y = 5$; vertical asymptote: $x = 4$, $x = -3$

7.   True

8. $(1, -5)$ and $(-1, -5)$

9.

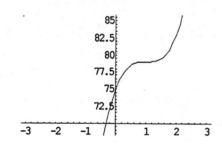

10.   A) $50x - \dfrac{x^2}{8}$

      B) $0 < x < 200$

      C) $200 < x < 360$

      D) $\$25$

      E) $\$5000$

11.   A) $\$2000$

      B) $\$70,500$

12. A) increasing

B) $0 < s < 50$

C) $50.00

13. A) increasing

B) $0 < s < 100$

C) $100.00

14. $72,750

15. Maximum price at hour 0 and minimum price at hour 3

1. $x < 1,\ x > 3$

2. 1

3. a local minimum

4. $(1, -2)$ is a relative minimum; $(-1, 2)$ is a relative maximum

5. A) $\left(\frac{-10}{3}, 0\right) \cup \left(\frac{10}{3}, \infty\right)$

   B) $\left(-\infty, \frac{-10}{3}\right) \cup \left(0, \frac{10}{3}\right)$

   C) $(0, 0)$

6. Absolute minimum: $(-1, -64)$, absolute maximum: $(3, 432)$

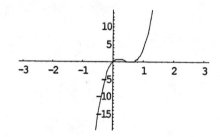

7. $(4, -136)$

8. A) 2

   B)

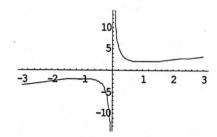

   C) $y \to -\infty$ as $x \to 0^-$

9. A) $50x - \dfrac{x^2}{8}$

    B) $0 < x < 200$

    C) $200 < x < 360$

    D) 25

    E) 5000

10. A) increasing

    B) $0 < s < 50$

    C) 50.00

11. A) increasing

    B) $0 < s < 100$

    C) 100.00

12. A) 6

    B) $48,000

13. Maximum at $x = 0$; minimum at $x = 8$

14. Maximum at $x = 0$; minimum at $x = -2$

15. radius $= \dfrac{10\sqrt{6}}{3}$ in.; $h = \dfrac{20\sqrt{3}}{3}$ in.

Tan Applied Calculus
Examination 4C-Answer Key

1.   True

2.   False

3.   None of the above

4. $\left(\pm\sqrt{\dfrac{1}{2}}, \dfrac{-1}{4}\right)$ are relative minima; (0, 0) is a relative maximum

5.   A) $\left(\dfrac{-10}{3}, 0\right) \cup \left(\dfrac{10}{3}, \infty\right)$

      B) $\left(-\infty, \dfrac{-10}{3}\right) \cup \left(0, \dfrac{10}{3}\right)$

      C) $(0, 0)$

6.   Horizontal asymptote: $y = 5$; vertical asymptote: $x = 4,\ x = -3$

7. y-axis symmetry

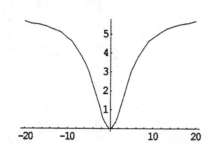

8.   Absolute minimum: $\left(-\sqrt{7}, -\dfrac{4\sqrt{7}}{7}\right)$, absolute maximum $\left(\sqrt{7}, \dfrac{4\sqrt{7}}{7}\right)$

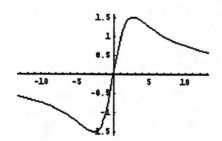

9.

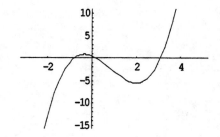

10.

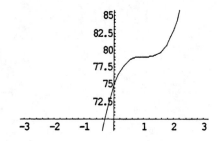

11.   A) $50x - \dfrac{x^2}{8}$ B) $0 < x < 200$

       C) $200 < x < 360$ D) $25

       E) $5000

12.   A) $125x - \dfrac{x^2}{4}$ B) $0 < x < 250$

       C) $250 < x < 400$ D) $62.50

       E) $15,625

13.   A)   increasing   B) $0 < s < 50$

       C) $50.00

14.   Maximum at $x = 0$; minimum at $x = -2$

15.   Maximum price at hour 0 and minimum price at hour 3.

1.

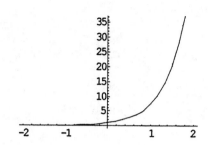

2. $\dfrac{\log 6 + 1}{2}$

3. $\ln 2,\ \ln 4$

4. $X^Z = Y$

5. $\dfrac{1}{8}$

6. A) $136.54   B) $85.07

7. ± 99

8. 5^{-3}

9. $\log \sqrt[3]{10} = \dfrac{1}{3}$

10. $\ln \dfrac{1}{e} = -1$

11. $e^5 = x$

12. $\dfrac{3e^{3x}}{(e^{3x}+1)^2}$

13. $2xe^{x^2} + 3x^2 e^{x^3}$

14. $\dfrac{8x}{4x^2+1}$

15. ≈ 38 million

1. $\frac{1}{3}(-6+\ln 9)$

2. 1

3.

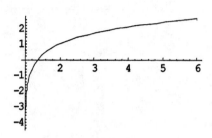

4. $e^9 - 5$

5. About 598 people

6. $\log_{\frac{1}{2}} \frac{5}{16} \approx 2$ years

7. \$17,617

8. A) \$600.08   B) \$58,015

9. $\frac{6xe^{6x} - e^{6x} - 9}{x^2}$

10. $f'(x) = -30x^2 e^{2x^3}$; $f''(x) = -30xe^{2x^3}(6x^3 + 2)$

11. $2xe^{x^2}$

12. $2xe^{x^2}(2x^2 + 1)$

13. $\frac{8x}{4x^2 + 1}$

14. 1

15. ≈ 38 million people

Tan Applied Calculus
Examination 5C-Answer Key

1. $\frac{1}{3}(-6 + \ln 9)$

2. $\frac{1}{3}(2 - \ln 19 + \ln 3) \approx 0.0514$

3.

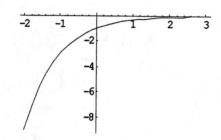

4. $X^Z = Y$

5. $\log_X Z = Y$

6. $\frac{1}{8}$

7. ± 99

8. $e^5 = x$

9. $\$22,081.62$

10. $\frac{3e^{3x}}{(e^{3x}+1)^2}$

11. A) $100e^{-0.05x}(1 - 0.05x)$ B)   2000

12. $x(3x+2)e^{3x}$

13. $2xe^{x^2} + 3x^2e^{x^3}$

14. 1

15. All of the above

1. $x^4 - 2x^3 + 3x^2 - 3x - 9$

2. $3x^2 + 24x^{\frac{3}{2}} + 60x + 72\sqrt{x} + 54\ln|x| + C$

3.   A)   \$1800   B)   loss of \$31

4. $\dfrac{x^6}{2} + C$

5. $-\dfrac{1}{4}t^{-4} + C$

6. $\dfrac{3}{5}x^{\frac{5}{3}} + 2x + 3x^{\frac{1}{3}} + C$

7. $x^4 + 2x^3 - x^2 + 5x + 5$

8.   A) $\dfrac{255}{14}$ square units   B) $\dfrac{1355}{14}$ square units

      C) $\dfrac{2845}{171}$ square units

9. $0.1x^2 + 20x + 1500$

10. $20\dfrac{5}{6}$

11. $\dfrac{7}{3}$

12.   Area = 36 square units

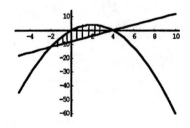

13. $\dfrac{9}{2}$ square units

14.   1.086161269

15.   \$140,000

Tan Applied Calculus
Examination 6B-Answer Key

1. $\frac{2}{15}x^{\frac{3}{2}}(3x+10)+C$

2. $4\sqrt{x}+C$

3. $\frac{2}{3}x^3 - \frac{3}{2}x^2 + 7x + C$

4. $C = 6x - 0.0002x^2 + 8500; \ C(12,000) = \$51,800$

5. $\frac{(\ln x)^2}{2} + C$

6. $\frac{(\ln y)^2}{4} + C$

7. $-\frac{(1-t^3)^6}{18} + C$

8. $0.2x^2 + 100x + 3500$

9. 31.0769

10. $\frac{13}{6}$

11. $\ln 5 - \ln 4$

12. $\ln\frac{\sqrt{2}}{2} - \frac{\sqrt{3}}{3} \approx 0.202732554$

13. Area = 9 square units

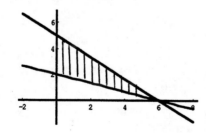

14. $38,900$

15. $\$2667$

1.   A)   \$1800   B)   loss of \$31

2. $\dfrac{1}{10x^2}\left(2x^7 + 5\right) + C$

3. $\dfrac{x^6}{2} + C$

4. $\dfrac{x^6}{6} + C$

5. $x^4 + 2x^3 - x^2 + 5x + 5$

6. $-\dfrac{1}{96}\left(12 - 6x^2\right)^8 + C$

7. $\dfrac{1}{3}\ln\left|x^3 + 6x\right| + C$

8.   0.40

9.   A) $\dfrac{1}{14}\displaystyle\int_{9}^{16}\dfrac{du}{\sqrt{u}}$ B) $\dfrac{1}{7}$

10. $\dfrac{20}{3}$

11. $\dfrac{1}{3}$ square unit

12.   \$68,256

13. $C(x) = 25,000 + 500x + \dfrac{31}{4}x^2$

14.   \$917.15

15.   \$28,402.54

1. $-\dfrac{x}{\sqrt{64x^2-1}}+C$

2. $\dfrac{x^4}{16}(4\ln x-1)+C$

3. $\dfrac{e^{5x}}{25}(5x-1)+C$

4. $x-\dfrac{1}{6}\ln\left|1-3e^{6x}\right|+C$

5. $2e^x+xe^x+C$

6. 3

7. 0.8862

8. 1.913972394

9. 0.534722222

10. 1.899751940

11. $\displaystyle\int_{1}^{\infty}\dfrac{1}{x^3}\,dx$

12. 1

13. Does not exist

14. $\dfrac{1}{32}$

15. A)   0.517   B)   0.182

1. $4 \ln 4 - 3$

2. $\dfrac{x^4}{16}(4\ln x - 1) + C$

3. $\ln\left|x + \sqrt{x^2 - 2}\right| + C$

4. $\dfrac{e^{5x}}{25}(5x - 1) + C$

5. $x - \dfrac{1}{6}\ln\left|1 - 3e^{6x}\right| + C$

6. 3

7. 0.3125

8. $\dfrac{2}{5}$

9. $\dfrac{7}{4}$ square units

10. $\displaystyle\int_{1}^{\infty} \dfrac{1}{x^3}\,dx$

11. 2

12. 1000

13. 1

14. $\dfrac{1}{32}$

15. $\dfrac{1}{8}$

Tan Applied Calculus
Examination 7C-Answer Key

1. $(8x-7)e^x - 8e^x + C$

2. $\frac{x}{2}\ln x - \frac{x}{2} + C$

3. $3\ln 3 - 2$

4. $\frac{e^{5x}}{25}(5x-1) + C$

5. 0.8862

6. 16.4

7. 1.913972394

8. 0.500417611

9. $\frac{7}{4}$ square units

10. $\int_1^\infty \frac{1}{x^4}dx$

11. 2

12. 2

13. 1

14. Does not exist

15. A) 0.517   B) 0.182

1. $6x - 8xy$

2. $-\dfrac{100x}{(x^2+y^2)^2}$

3.   A) $(2,1)$ and $(2,-5)$

     B)   Relative maximum: $f(2,-5) = 219$; saddle point at $(2,1)$

4.   A)   No critical points

     B)   Second Derivative does not apply

5.   Saddle point at $(0, 0, 0)$ and relative minimum at $(\sqrt[3]{2}, \sqrt[3]{4}, -4)$

6.   64

7. $\displaystyle\int_0^e \int_0^{\ln y} \frac{1}{\ln y}\, dx\, dy = e - 1$

8.   Cost of \$42 for 2 hr. of construction and 2 hr. of finishing

9. $y = \dfrac{12}{7}x + \dfrac{25}{7}$

10. $y = 2x + \dfrac{26}{3}$

11. $y = -4.58x + 92.67$

12. $y = 1.08484x + 53.73333$

13. 900 units of labor; 120 units of capital

14. -162

15. $\dfrac{e^2}{2}\left(e^8 - 1\right)$

Tan Applied Calculus
Examination 8B-Answer Key

1. $420\pi \approx 1319$

2. $\dfrac{\partial f}{\partial x} = 4x^3 + 2y;\ \dfrac{\partial f}{\partial y} = -12y^2 + 2x$

3. $10x - 8xy$

4. $2xe^{x^2+y^2}$

5. $\dfrac{5y^2}{(x+y)^2}$

6. $-\dfrac{10y^2}{(x+y)^3}$

7. $x = y = 4$

8. $4x^2 - 8x + \dfrac{28}{3}$

9. 5 projects in Miami and 3 in Tampa

10. Cost of $42 for 2 hr. of construction and 2 hr. of finishing

11. $y = -1.12x + 204.19$

12. 900 units of labor; 120 units of capital

13. -162

14. 144,971 people

15. $\dfrac{1}{3}$

1. 4.4998

2 17,082.17

3. 300

4. $\dfrac{\partial f}{\partial x} = 2x \ln(x^2 + y^3) + \dfrac{2x^3}{x^2+y^3}$; $\dfrac{\partial f}{\partial y} = \dfrac{3x^2 y^2}{x^2 + y^3}$

5. -14

6. $-\dfrac{10y^2}{(x+y)^3}$

7. A) $(2, 1)$ and $(2, -5)$

   B) Relative maximum: $f(2, -5) = 219$; saddle point at $(2, 1)$

8. $\left(-\dfrac{16}{5}, -\dfrac{14}{5}, -\dfrac{82}{5}\right)$ is a relative minimum for f

9. $\left(-\dfrac{3\sqrt{5}}{5}, \dfrac{6\sqrt{5}}{5}, 4 + 3\sqrt{5}\right)$

10. $\displaystyle\int_0^2 \int_{x^2}^4 3xy \, dy \, dx = 32$

11. $\displaystyle\int_0^e \int_0^{\ln y} \dfrac{1}{\ln y} dx \, dy = e - 1$

12. 54

13. $\dfrac{47}{840}$

14. $y = 1.75x + 2$

15. $y = 1.4x + 2$

1. $-\frac{1}{y} = x^2 - x + C$

2. $\ln|y| = -\frac{2}{x} + C$

3. $y^3 = 6x^2 + 3x + C$

4. $x^{10}(y^2 + 9) = C$

5. $\ln|y| = \frac{1}{2x^2} - \frac{1}{2}$

6. $\frac{dx}{dt} = x(80 - x)$

7. $y = -\frac{5}{4}x^4 + \frac{4}{3}$

8. 9888 fungi

9. A) $40\left(1 - e^{-\frac{3t}{10}}\right)$ pounds

   B) $40\left(1 - e^{-\frac{15}{2}}\right) \approx 40$ pounds

   C) 40 pounds

10. $\frac{dA}{dt} = 0.09A$

11. $y^2 = \frac{2}{3}x^3 + 46$

12. $6\ln|y| + 12y^{-1} - 9y^{-2} = 2x^3 + 3$

13. $\frac{1}{40}(2x - 1)^5(19 - 10x) + C$

14. 51 years

15. $\approx 133,000$

1. A) $y' = C\left(8x^3 e^{2x^4}\right)$ and $y' - 8x^3 y = C\left(8x^3 e^{2x^4}\right) - 8x^3\left(Ce^{2x^4}\right) = 0$

   B) $y = \frac{1}{3}e^{2(x^4-1)}$

2. $3y^5 + \frac{5}{y^3} = -45e^{-x^2} + C$

3. $x^{10}\left(y^2 + 9\right) = C$

4. $\frac{dx}{dt} = x(80 - x)$

5. $y = -\frac{5}{4}x^4 + \frac{4}{3}$

6. A) $40\left(1 - e^{-\frac{3t}{10}}\right)$ pounds

   B) $40\left(1 - e^{-\frac{15}{2}}\right) \approx 40$ pounds

   C) 40 pounds

7. 1.0905

8. $y^2 = \frac{1}{3}x^2 - 2x + C$

9. $2\sqrt{y} = \frac{x^3}{3} + C$

10. $y^3 = 3e^{x+3} + e^3 - 3e^4$

11. $\frac{1}{4}xe^{4x} - \frac{1}{16}e^{4x} + C$

12. $-\frac{1}{4}(5x + 3)e^{-4x} - \frac{5}{16}e^{-4x} + C$

13. 51 years

14. $T(t) = M\left(1 - e^{-kt}\right)$

15. $\approx 133,000$

1. $-\frac{1}{y} = x^2 - x + C$

2. A) $y' = C\left(8x^3 e^{2x^4}\right)$ and $y' - 8x^3 y = C\left(8x^3 e^{2x^4}\right) - 8x^3\left(Ce^{2x^4}\right) = 0$

   B) $y = \frac{1}{3}e^{2(x^4-1)}$

3. $x^2 + 2y^2 = 12$

4. $\frac{dx}{dt} = x(80 - x)$

5. 389 students

6. A) $40\left(1 - e^{-\frac{3t}{10}}\right)$ pounds

   B) $40\left(1 - e^{-\frac{15}{2}}\right) \approx 40$ pounds

   C) 40 pounds

7. 1.0905

8. $Me^{x^2 + x}$

9. $y^2 = \frac{1}{3}x^2 - 2x + C$

10. $y^3 = 3e^{x+3} + C$

11. $x^3 - 2x^2 + 5x + 3$

12. $6\ln|y| + 12y^{-1} - 9y^{-2} = 2x^3 + 3$

13. $y^3 = 3e^{x+3} + e^3 - 3e^4$

14. $\frac{1}{4}xe^{4x} - \frac{1}{16}e^{4x} + C$

15. $(\ln x)\left(\frac{x^3}{x} + 2x^2 - 5x\right) - \frac{x^3}{9} - x^2 + 5x + C$

1. $P_4(x) = -\frac{1}{2} - \frac{1}{4}x - \frac{1}{8}x^2 - \frac{1}{16}x^3 - \frac{1}{32}x^4$

2. 5.0990

3. A) $a_n = n^3$

   B) Diverges

4. $\frac{52}{33}$

5. $R = 2;\ (-4, 0)$

6. $f(x) = -\frac{1}{9} - \frac{2}{9^2}x - \frac{2^2}{9^3}x^2 - \ldots \frac{2^n}{9^{n+1}}x^n - \ldots;\ \left(-\frac{2}{9}, \frac{2}{9}\right)$

7. $f(x) = 2\left(6^2x - 6^4x^3 + 6^6x^5 - \ldots + (-1)^{n+1}6^{2n}x^{2n-1} + \ldots\right)$

8. 0.2983

1. $-\dfrac{9\pi}{4}$ radians

2. 600°

3. $\dfrac{\sqrt{2}}{2}$

4. $\dfrac{\pi}{3}, \dfrac{5\pi}{3}$

5.

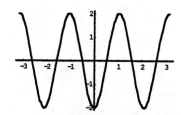

6. $\sec x \tan^2 x + \sec^3 x$

7. $y = \sqrt{2}\, x - \dfrac{\pi}{2\sqrt{2}} + \sqrt{2}$

8. High tide at 5:00 a.m. and 4:30 p.m.; low tide at 10:45 a.m. and 10:15 p.m.

9. $\sec x + C$

10. 13,773